宜興紫砂陶器

YIXING

PURPLE
CLAY
WARES

The K.S. Lo Collection,

Flagstaff House Museum of Tea Ware

茶具文物館羅桂祥珍藏

Produced by the Hong Kong Museum of Art of the
Leisure and Cultural Services Department
康樂及文化事務署
香港藝術館編製

宜興紫砂陶器

YIXING

PURPLE
CLAY
WARES

The K.S. Lo Collection,
Flagstaff House Museum of Tea Ware

茶具文物館羅桂祥珍藏

Published by the Leisure and Cultural Services Department, 1994
Second edition, revised, 2002 (1-2,000)
Produced by the Hong Kong Museum of Art
Copyright © 2002 Leisure and Cultural Services Department
All rights reserved

本刊物由康樂及文化事務署一九九四年首次編印
二○○二年再版（1-2,000）
香港藝術館編製
版權屬康樂及文化事務署所有 © 二○○二年
版權所有，未經許可不得翻印、節錄或轉載

ISBN 962-215-124-8

Hong Kong Museum of Art Production Team

Project Co-ordination
Anita Y.F. Wong, *Assistant Curator I*
Grace Y.S. Kwok, *Assistant Curator II*

Catalogue Design
Candy L.W. Choi, *Technical Officer I*

Photography
Joseph K.K. Kwan, *Technical Officer II*
Arthur K.L. Wong, *Photographer II*

香港藝術館工作小組

統籌
黃燕芳　一級助理館長
郭恩生　二級助理館長

目錄設計
蔡麗華　一級技術主任

攝影
關家駒　二級技術主任
黃國良　二級攝影員

Tea, though ridiculed by those who are
naturally coarse in their nervous sensibilities...
will always be the favoured beverage of the
intellectual.

Thomas De Quincey (1785 – 1859)
Confessions of an English Opium Eater

茶．

香葉．嫩芽．

慕詩客．愛僧家．

碾雕白玉．羅織紅紗．

銚煎黃蕊色．碗轉曲塵花．

夜後邀陪明月．晨前命對朝霞．

洗盡古今人不倦．將至醉後豈堪誇．

唐代．元稹〈茶〉詩

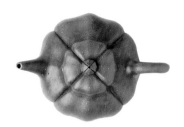

Contents

Preface
Chief Curator, Hong Kong Museum of Art
10

The Flagstaff House Museum of Tea Ware
Dr K.S. Lo
12

Yixing Wares in the K.S. Lo Collection
Anita Y. F. Wong
18

Plates
50

Index
168

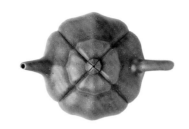

目錄

序

香港藝術館總館長

11

茶具文物館

羅桂祥博士

15

羅桂祥珍藏宜興紫砂陶器

黃燕芳

35

圖版

50

索引

168

Preface

As early as the Tang dynasty, tea was taken by the Chinese as a drink during leisure. The method of preparing a cup of tea differed in different periods and the vessels used in the preparation also varied from time to time. Our present method of steeping tea leaves in hot water started in the Ming dynasty (1368 – 1644) and so were the teapots which bear a spout, a handle and a cover to retain the heat of water.

Ever since the Ming dynasty, the Yixing county of Jiangsu province has been well-known for producing teapots of sandy quality, in colours of purple, yellow, red, green and black, with or without carved or painted decorations. These vessels are often called Yixing teapots or *zisha* (purple clay) teapots. Most of them bear the signature or the seal mark of the potter, which is another characteristic. It is believed that Yixing teapots can retain the colour, flavour and aroma of tea for a longer period of time than any other kinds of teapot and therefore, they are much sought after by tea connoisseurs.

The travelling exhibition of Yixing wares from the K.S. Lo Collection to four museums in North America, namely the Phoenix Art Museum of Arizona, the Chinese Culture Center of San Francisco, the Indianapolis Museum of Art and the Royal Ontario Museum in Toronto from May 1990 to January 1992 was a great success. The exhibition was very well received and it had successfully introduced to the western world the art of pottery making in Yixing. We are pleased to present the same exhibition to museums in the United Kingdom, Europe and Southeast Asia, commencing in the fall of 1994.

The exhibition features a selection of 118 pieces of Yixing wares from the K.S. Lo Collection housed in the Flagstaff House Museum of Tea Ware, which includes teapots, tea cups, figurines and objects for the scholar's studio dated from late Ming dynasty to the present day. We are pleased to share with art lovers and tea connoisseurs abroad what Dr Lo shared with the public in Hong Kong when he made his generous donation to the Urban Council in 1981.

I would like to express my gratitude to the staff of each participating venue who have made this tour possible. Special thanks are due to Dr K.S. Lo who is undoubtedly the moving force behind the touring of the show. We are most grateful to Dr Lo for his article on the history of Flagstaff House and his continual support to the Flagstaff House Museum of Tea Ware, under the Hong Kong Museum of Art, Urban Council, Hong Kong.

Gerard C. C. Tsang
Chief Curator, Hong Kong Museum of Art

———— 序 ————

　　早在唐代開始，喝茶已經成為中國人生活消閒的一種風尚。隨着備茶方法的改變，嗜茶者對茶具的要求亦不斷地提高。自明代開始，流行以熱水冲泡散茶的方法，就像今天我們泡茶一樣。因此，有流有把有蓋的茶壺便應運而生。

　　宜興茶壺是江蘇省宜興縣的產品，早在明代已經大量生產。宜興茶壺質堅而帶有砂粒，顏色有紫、黑、黃、紅、綠等。裝飾手法大略有刻畫和以琺瑯繪畫山水花鳥圖案等，也有素身無飾的。宜興茶壺有保持茶湯的色、香和味的特點，因此受到嗜茶者所珍愛。明清兩代迄今，宜興製陶名家輩出，他們都喜歡在其作品刻上或印上名字，成為宜興陶藝的一大特色。

　　是次展出的宜興陶器均選自市政局香港藝術館分館茶具文物館的羅桂祥珍藏。在一九九〇年五月至一九九二年一月期間，這批藏品曾於北美洲的美國鳳凰城美術博物館、舊金山中華文化中心、印第安納波利斯藝術博物館及加拿大多倫多安大略皇家博物館巡迴展出，大受當地人士歡迎，並成功地把宜興陶藝推介到北美各地。我們感到萬分雀躍能在一九九四年秋季開始，將這批珍藏再度在英國、歐洲及東南亞等地的博物館巡迴展出。

　　是次展覽展示一百一十八件宜興陶器，包括了由明代至現今製作的各式茶具、雕塑及文玩。羅桂祥博士於一九八一年把收藏的茶具慷慨捐贈予香港市政局，讓廣大市民有欣賞的機會；今天我們深感榮幸，能夠與各地熱愛藝術茗趣的人士，分享這份樂趣。

　　是次巡迴展覽，荷蒙各參展機構及有關工作人員提供協助，更得到羅桂祥博士鼎力推動，使統籌工作得以順利進行，本人謹致謝忱。本目錄更承蒙羅博士撰寫茶具文物館的歷史一文，加以羅博士多年來對香港茶具文物館的支持和鼓勵，本人謹此再次表示衷心的謝意。

曾柱昭
香港藝術館總館長

The Flagstaff House Museum of Tea Ware

Dr K.S. Lo

The Flagstaff House Museum of Tea Ware was opened on 27 January 1984. It is a specialized museum devoted exclusively to the display of tea and tea wares. The founding collections comprise of two parts: Yixing ware, and other ceramic wares dating from 1000 B.C. to the 1990s. The total number of items is slightly over 600, divided almost equally between the two.

Flagstaff House Museum of Tea Ware
茶具文物館

If such a museum is unique, so is the building which houses its collections. It was built in 1844 as the official residence of the Commander-In-Chief of the British Forces in Hong Kong, hence the name Flagstaff House. In 1978, the whole of Victoria Barracks, where the building is situated, was returned to the Hong Kong Government by the British Forces. It was then decided to hand over Flagstaff House to the Urban Council to be preserved as a building of antiquity. By the establishment of the Museum of Tea Ware at Flagstaff House, the dual purpose of preserving the building and the ancient Chinese culture of tea drinking for the people of Hong Kong has been achieved.

Within a short span of 10 years, the Museum has become a popular tourist attraction, a centre of research, and a catalyst for the new development of Yixing teapots. The interest in tea drinking and the production of teapots the Museum stimulates is not confined to Hong Kong alone, but has spread to China and Taiwan. Locally, it has created a new interest among the younger generation who might never have given a thought to the old tradition of tea drinking had they not visited the Museum. But having done so, they are encouraged to experiment on different ways of preparing tea, and then to try their hands in the making of teapots and tea cups. Some of them showed great creativity by coming up with new shapes, new textures and new decorations. The Museum has organized three competitions of the works of our local budding potters. The response was excellent, the one held in 1992 attracting as many as 195 entries. The standard on the whole is high. Indeed, I am overwhelmed by the creativity and ingenuity shown by these young potters who, if given proper training, could one day stand shoulder to shoulder with the best potters in China and elsewhere.

Flagstaff House in 1981, vacated for conversion into the Museum of Tea Ware
一九八一年，空置的旗杆屋正待改建。

Flagstaff House Museum of Tea Ware in 1984 (Note that the porch at the main entrance was deconstructed)
一九八四年，茶具文物館落成時外貌
（注意正門前的有蓋門廊已被拆除）

Perhaps, the greatest influence the Museum has exerted is on Taiwan where tea drinking has now become a vogue, and the collecting of Yixing teapots a status symbol. There are today hundreds of tea houses in Taibei where one can meet friends and have a chat over a leisurely cup of tea. It is the revival of the old tradition where scholars and the merchant gentry congregated in tea houses to discuss poetry or business. A related phenomenon is the collecting of Yixing teapots by those who can afford to do so. It has now developed into a friendly rivalry as to who has collected the largest and the best.

The vogue of tea drinking in Taiwan has also brought prosperity to the Yixing teapot industry. When I first visited Yixing in 1979, there was only one factory with 400 to 600 potters making *zisha* teapots. The pots made then were for the mass market, rather roughly finished and without any decoration, except for the mark "Yixing, China" on the base. The price ranged from a low of three *renminbi* to a high of 100 *renminbi* for a pot. Today, there are over twenty *zisha* factories employing about 10,000 potters; all busily making teapots for export. What was a dying handicraft not so long ago has today become one of the fastest-growing and most vigorous industries in China.

In 1990, a selection of 118 pieces of Yixing ware from the Museum collection were sent on a travelling exhibition in North America. It started off with the Phoenix Art Museum in Arizona; from there to the Chinese Culture Center of San Francisco, the Indianapolis Museum of Art and finally, the Royal Ontario Museum in Toronto, Canada. The exhibits attracted a great deal of interest everywhere they went. Those who have seen these beautiful teapots made by the Ming and Qing master potters wanted to buy some either for use or for display, and thus rekindled a universal interest in Yixing.

Entrance hall of the Flagstaff House
Museum of Tea Ware
茶具文物館進口大堂

I am pleased to learn that the Museum of Tea Ware has organized another touring exhibition of Yixing to Europe this year, starting with the British Museum in London. I hope it will prove to be equally successful as the previous one to North America.

茶具文物館

羅桂祥博士

　　茶具文物館在一九八四年一月二十七日正式開放，是一座以茶及茶具為專題的博物館。館內基本藏品分為兩部份：一是宜興茶具，餘為陶瓷茶具，年代由公元前一千年至一九九○年代。兩部份藏品數量相若，總數超過六百件。

　　收藏這批珍品的建築物更是獨特。它建於一八四四年，為駐港英軍司令官邸，故此命名為旗桿屋。一九七八年，駐港英軍把整個域多利兵房（即旗桿屋現址）交還港府，後者

Flagstaff House Museum of Tea Ware
茶具文物館

決議把旗桿屋這幢富有歷史價值的建築物撥歸市政局管轄。重修旗桿屋並設立茶具文物館正符合爲香港市民保存古蹟及發揚傳統中國茶藝的雙重目的。

　　在短短十年間，茶具文物館發展爲一個極受歡迎的旅遊勝地，也是研究及推動宜興茶具發展的中心。其對茗茶風尙及茶壺製作的積極提倡，不只局限於香港，更遍及中國及台灣。對於本地年輕一代，他們通過欣賞館內展品得以認識傳統中國茶藝，不但對中國歷代飲茶風俗發生興趣，更可鼓勵他們嘗試設計茶具，在型制、質感及裝飾上表達創新意念。茶具文物館所舉辦的三屆陶瓷茶具創作比賽，都得到本地陶藝家的踴躍支持。在一九九二年比賽中，更收到一百九十五件參選作品，而且水準很高。本人十分佩服這群年輕人的創造力和別出心裁的設計。我想假以時日，這些年青藝術家必能與中國及世界各地優秀陶藝家看齊。

Flagstaff House Museum of Tea Ware
茶具文物館

　　茶具文物館的成立對台灣的影響至爲深遠。品茗在台灣社會蔚成風氣，蒐集宜興茶壺更是地位的象徵。單在台北市已開設有數以百間中、小型茶藝館，茶客可聯同兩三知己在館內消閒聊天。這情景正回復過往文人雅聚品茶、研究詩詞或商討公事的古老傳統。基於品茗風尙大行其道，一般經濟上許可的人都開始收購宜興茶壺，彼此之間更爭相競投，以求得到最豐富及最佳的收藏。

Entrance hall of the Flagstaff House
Museum of Tea Ware
茶具文物館進口大堂

　　另一方面，這股熱潮也推動了宜興茶具工業的發展。在一九七九年，本人初次遊覽宜興，當時僅有一所紫砂工藝廠，聘用四百至六百位陶工。所製成的茶壺供應普羅大眾，壺身只稍作修整而且缺乏裝飾，壺底蓋上「中國宜興」字樣，價錢最低的茶壺只值三元人民幣，最名貴的也只是一百元。但時至今日，在宜興已有超過二十所紫砂工藝廠，聘用陶工達一萬人，製成品廣銷外地。這門在不久以前日漸衰落的手工業，現今已成爲中國發展得最迅速及最蓬勃的工業之一。

在一九九〇年，茶具文物館安排一批爲數一百一十八件宜興陶器到北美洲巡迴展出。第一站是亞利桑那州的鳳凰城美術博物館，然後分別在舊金山中華文化中心、印第安納波利斯藝術博物館和加拿大多倫多的安大略皇家博物館展出，到處都廣受歡迎。不少欣賞過展出的明、清兩代優美茗壺的人士，都千方百計蒐集紫砂茶具自用或用以收藏，令宜興陶藝引起廣泛的關注。

本人很高興知悉茶具文物館將在今年籌備另一個宜興巡迴展覽到歐洲展出，首站是英國倫敦的大英博物館。本人預祝是次展覽正如在北美一般，展出成功。

Yixing Wares in the K.S. Lo Collection

Anita Y.F. Wong

The K.S. Lo Collection housed in the Flagstaff House Museum of Tea Ware provides a very good basis for systematic research and popular appreciation of traditional and contemporary tea culture with a comprehensive assemblage of Chinese ceramic tea vessels. Yixing wares dated from the sixteenth century to the present day comprise half of the Collection. Although the attribution and dating of some ancient pieces are still pending further research, the beauty and vitality of this anthology of purple clay wares are unquestionable. Dr Lo's energetic collecting and research on Yixing wares[1] have promoted and stimulated the appreciation of this

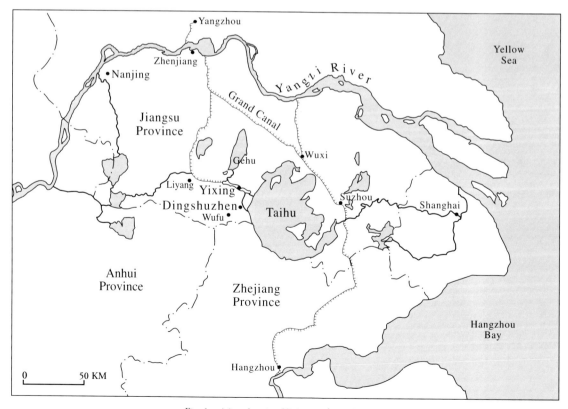

Fig. 1   Map showing Yixing and its vicinity

unique art form both in Hong Kong and abroad. As this is the tenth birthday of the Flagstaff House Museum of Tea Ware, we would like to share with tea lovers and art connoisseurs the chance to comprehend the fine heritage of Chinese tea culture through this selection of Yixing wares from the K.S. Lo Collection.

Yixing, also known as Jingxi and Yangxian[2], is known as the Pottery Capital of China. Situated to the western end of Lake Tai, this small county in Jiangsu province has been famous for its production of purple clay wares for several centuries (*Fig. 1*).

Purple clay

Purple clay is a common name for the clay material excavated from the mountains of Yixing. The area from Dingshan to Shushan is the centre for the production of purple clay wares known as Dingshuzhen (*Fig. 2*).[3] Shushan produced fine pottery while Dingshan was known for its big and coarse ware.

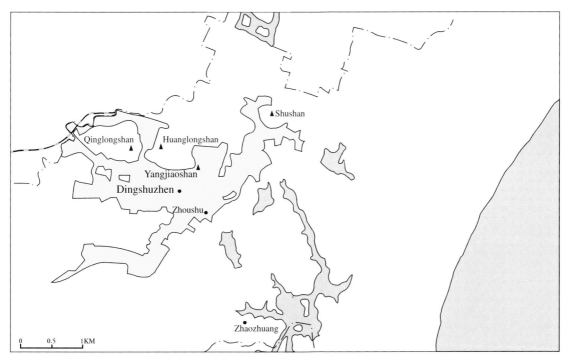

Fig. 2   Map of Dingshuzhen

The clay is fine grained and highly malleable. It contains a very high iron content of over 9% and has remarkable plasticity, which is perfect for minute, precise modelling of tea wares.[4] Since it did not soften satisfactorily with the addition of water, purple clay is unsuited to the potter's wheel. As a result, the Yixing tradition centres on hand-building pots rather than throwing them. Yixing purple clay wares are principally shaped by the "paddling"[5] and "luting"[6] techniques, specially developed by local potters for this unique material. Yixing potters have also designed a comprehensive set of tools made of bamboo, wood, horn and metal for the making of purple clay wares, which are still used today (*Fig. 3*).

After firing at a temperature of about 1,200°C, the clay has very good absorption of water and porous density. These qualities make it ideal for the production of teapots for brewing tea. Yixing teapots are very often left unglazed and undecorated because of their interesting shapes and textures which are aesthetically pleasing in themselves. In addition, the plain surface of the pot can keep the warm porosity of the clay material that is highly retentive of tea flavour, colour and aroma. It can be noticed that the longer the teapot is used, the brighter it shines with the creation of a layer of "patina" on the surface and in the interior which makes the brewed tea more fragrant.

Principally, purple clay can be divided into *zisha* (purple clay), *zhusha* (cinnabar or orange-red clay) and *benshanlü ni* (yellow buff-coloured clay, also known as *duan ni*) (*Fig. 4*). These clay materials can be used independently or mixed together with mineral colours to achieve a wide range of earth colours in different tones of brown, red and yellow. Dark green and blackish purple are early twentieth-century innovations.[7]

Fig. 3   Tools used by Yixing potters. From left to right: horn scraper, iron cutter, sheet cutter, turn-table, mallet, spatulas of different sizes.

Fig. 4   Raw material of red, purple and yellow clay (left) and products (right)

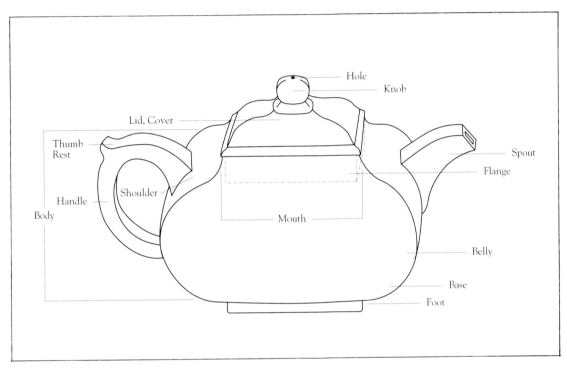

Fig. 5 Different sections of a teapot

Characteristics of Yixing wares

Yixing ware is well known for superb craftsmanship, manifold shapes and elegant colours. Apart from its artistic value, it has a unique practical function for the preparation of tea. Although the commonest and best received type of Yixing pottery is the teapot (*Fig. 5*), objects for the scholar's studio such as seal paste box (Plate 9), brush pots (Plates 10, 14), brush rest (Plate 19), palette and water holder (Plate 88) and water dropper (Plate 95) as well as sculptures (Plates 92, 94) and other miscellaneous items like a pair of pillows (Plate 69) are produced and represented in the K.S. Lo Collection.

In terms of varieties of shapes, Yixing wares can be classified into geometric, naturalistic and segmented forms.

Geometric wares are those based on spheres, cylinders, cubes, rectangular prisms and other geometric forms. This category is one of the most popular shapes in the design of Yixing teapots and many typical examples can be drawn from the K.S. Lo Collection (Plates 1, 7, 11,

15, 17, 26, 32, 33, 34, 41, 42, 46, 48, 49, 56, 57, 58, 60, 62, 63, 71, 73, 76–86, 97, 99, 114–118). These plain or inscription-decorated items in geometric forms are very well received by tea connoisseurs for their simplicity and elegance. Another special feature of this category is the design of overhead instead of side handles which greatly enhances the graceful outlook of the geometric forms (Plates 27, 37, 67, 68, 89, 98).

Naturalistic wares are modelled after motifs from nature such as tree trunks, plant and floral forms. These are the most creative and decorative types and best exemplify the potter's fine sense of imagination and keen observation of nature. There are many naturalistic works in the K.S. Lo Collection. The "Three Friends of Winter", namely pine, bamboo and prunus, are one of the most popular motifs. They are used either for the design of shape or as decorative elements on Yixing teapots (Pine: Plate 14; Bamboo: Plates 12, 28, 48, 49, 56, 57, 70, 72, 88, 100; Prunus: Plates 19, 39, 50, 108). Among them, the creativity of shape can be witnessed in Chen Mingyuan's brush rest (Plate 19) which is modelled after a gnarled prunus branch and Chen Zhongmei's treatment of bundled bamboo as a teapot (Plate 12). Other instances include the teapot in shape of Buddha's hand citron (Plate 87) by Fan Jinfu, an early twentieth-century potter, the water dropper made by a contemporary female potter Jiang Rong (Plate 95) and the teapot in form of lotus seed-pod (Plate 96) by another contemporary female potter Wang Yinxian. Their works demonstrate a potter's great technical skill and power of minute observation from nature.

Segmented wares consist of objects in shape of stylized flowers and lobed plants. This kind of veined wares require the precision of design, skilful modelling and naturalistic treatment of the floral and melon shapes. In the K.S. Lo Collection, there are a number of segmented wares in floral shapes such as narcissus (Plate 2), magnolia (Plate 3), chrysanthemum (Plate 6) and sweet osmanthus (Plate 16). When moulding a segmented teapot, potters should achieve the design that the lid fits the body tightly and also turns around smoothly.

There is also a wide variety of decorations on Yixing ware, with pieces painted in slip (Plates 41, 52) or covered with robin's egg glaze (Plates 33, 34), as well as decorated with designs moulded in relief (Plates 10, 14, 87, 95, 96, 100) and reticulated openwork (Plate 28). In the eighteenth century, Yixing wares were sometimes decorated with enamel, mostly in the *fencai* (*famille-rose*) colourings (Plates 40, 50, 53, 54, 64, 107). The slip decoration and enamel application are used to produce colour-contrast.

The Yixing potters are also good at imitating the art forms of ancient bronzes (Plates 8, 36) and stone stelae (Plate 43). The silver-inlay wares innovated by contemporary potters (Plate 99) are also highly appreciated because of their luxurious outlook. This decorative method first appeared in ancient Chinese bronzes but was adopted and revived by contemporary Yixing potters.

Fig. 6 Teapot by Cheng Shouzhen (Plate 84) showing location of seal marks

Fig. 7 Teapot by Gu Shaopei (Plate 100) showing location of seal marks

Fig. 8 Thai marks on the flange of Plates 117, 118

One particular precious feature of Yixing wares is that they generally carry a clear, identifying potter's seal or signature. All the purple clay wares are artist-signed or stamped with individual seals of the potter, inscriber and designer (Plate 46). The seals are sometimes engraved in the centre of the base, stamped under the spout, pressed on the lower part or the underside of the handle, or found on the interior of the lid. (*Figs 6, 7*) Sometimes, the mark is even found on the flange of the lid. (*Fig.* 8) In rare cases, the seal is stamped on the interior bottom of the teapot encased with pewter (Plates 44, 45). (*Figs 9, 10*) During the Ming dynasty, the name was incised on the pot in regular script (Plates 1–5, 7–9, 11–14), but that was eventually replaced by the imprint of carved seals, stamps and other marks or inscriptions which helps to identify individual potters, inscribers, dating or geographical locations of production.

Fig. 9 Seal mark on the interior bottom of Plate 44

Fig. 10 Seal mark on the interior bottom of Plate 45

This unique feature in the history of Chinese ceramics marks the importance of individuality and personal contribution in artistic expression. It also confirms the artistic value of the products and the social status of the potters. The seals and inscriptions also provide reliable information on the authenticity of purple clay wares and the potters' biographies.

Development of Yixing pottery

Yixing wares comprise half of the founding collection of the Flagstaff House Museum of Tea Ware. They are internationally well-known for their simplicity and rustic qualities as well as high artistic and functional values. The popularity and rapid development of Yixing wares in the past three hundred years are closely related to the advocation and participation of scholars and intellectuals during the Ming and Qing dynasties.

The production of Yixing ware can be traced far beyond the Ming dynasty. Sherds were discovered in 1976 in the Song-dated (960–1125) dragon kiln[8] site near Yangjiaoshan in Yixing.[9] From the mid Ming dynasty, Yixing teapots became very popular until the present day, when the steeped tea method came into fashion. The importance of Yixing pottery since the mid Ming period can be accounted for by the fact that tea was prepared by brewing with boiling water instead of cooking in pots as in the case of previous periods, thus requiring a tea vessel of high temperature-resistance and air-permeability. As a result, the teapot came into being and became commonly used.

The discovery of clay at Yixing is traditionally attributed to an eccentric monk. He shouted one day, "Riches and honours for sale!" The people laughed at him, and he retorted, "If you will not buy honours, why not buy riches?" Then he led the villagers to the place where purple clay was to be found. The villagers returned to the site later and found clay which "was variegated and as beautiful as brocade".[10] In the K.S. Lo Collection, there is a piece of sculpture of this monk by Xu Xiutang, a famous contemporary Yixing potter-sculptor (Plate 92).

The first names associated with Yixing teapots are the old monk of the Jinsha Temple[11] and Gongchun, the young servant of Wu Yishan.[12] It is said that Gongchun first learned the secrets of the old monk of the Jinsha Temple when attending his master, a *jinshi* of the Zhengde period (1506–1521), who came to the Temple for instruction. Gongchun imitated the technique of the priest and made a teapot in shape of knur of an old gingko tree. One example of such "Gongchun teapot" in the K.S. Lo Collection is a copied work (Plate 61) by Huang Yulin, a famous potter of the late Qing period, who is well-known for his copies of classic prototypes of Gongchun teapots.

The works of Gongchun were described as being of a chestnut colour and are dignified and elegant in shape, like ancient metal ware.[13] One elegant and simple pot dated 1513 which can be attributed to Gongchun is the earliest dated piece in the K.S. Lo Collection (Plate 1). This is a shape modelled after Yongle-dated teapots made in Jingdezhen.[14] The body is divided into six shallow lobes. One trace of its early dating is the joining of the body at the shoulder which illustrates that the pot was made in two halves. Indeed, both the monk and Gongchun are the two important historical figures who initiated the professionalism and artistic treatment of Yixing pottery.

Shi Peng was another famous potter in the late Ming period. He was one of the four masters of the Wanli period (1573–1620).[15] In the K.S. Lo Collection, there is a teapot in shape of a water-chestnut flower with his engraved signature (Plate 2) which reflects his delicate and classical style. The cover of this typical segmented or vein ware is very well-fitted, with a thumb rest designed on the handle for more convenient usage.

Shi Dabin, son of Shi Peng and a student of Gongchun, was the foremost artist-potter living from the Wanli period of the Ming dynasty to the Kangxi period (1662–1722) of the Qing dynasty. Sources of the period described him as an austere and elegant man as well as a demanding potter, who destroyed his lesser pieces and added bits of fired pottery to his clay mixtures. As a result, there are not many extant works by him. In the K.S. Lo Collection, there are several pieces which can be attributed to Shi Dabin. One is the teapot in the shape of a monk's cap with lotus crown (Plate 4) which was formerly in the Percival David Foundation of Chinese Art in London. This shape was adopted from a prototype of the previous eras and was originally derived from the shape of the Tibetan metal ewer.[16] Other outstanding works of Shi include the teapot of magnolia shape (Plate 3) and the teapot in the shape of a square seal wrapped in cloth (Plate 5). The latter piece was commissioned by Xiang Yuanbian[17], the great merchant collector and patron of the late Ming period, whose studio name was Molin Tang as inscribed on the base of the pot. There are presently several teapots of Shi Dabin excavated from Ming tombs.[18] It is said that his earliest works are in imitation of Gongchun and are known for their simplicity and delicate craftsmanship. In his later years he became acquainted with scholars like Chen Jiru[19], who inspired him to make teapots of smaller size. This marked the beginning of the collaboration between scholar-officials and Yixing potters in the following decades.

Li Maolin, commonly known as Li Yangxin, was also active during the Wanli period. He resembled Shi Peng in his adherence to the delicate style of Gongchun. The teapot of chrysanthemum shape supported by four *ruyi*-shaped feet (Plate 6) well illustrates his skilled craftsmanship in a subtle and elegant style. Li Zhongfang, his elder son, was a student of Shi Dabin. Plate 7 is a teapot of square shape with curved sides which is typical of his delicate and refined work.

Xu Youquan, another potter of the Wanli period, made innovations in the mixing of clay and typology of teapots. He also made contributions in imitation of ancient bronze vessels (Plate 8). A contemporary of Xu, Chen Zhongmei was a native of Wuyuan in Jiangxi province, who first worked as a potter at Jingdezhen. After entering the purple clay industry, he was noted for his precision of craftsmanship in the overall form and the design of cover as reflected by the teapot in shape of bundled bamboo dated 1613 (Plate 12).

Shao Wenyin and Chen Yongqing were two other potters active in the Wanli period. The teapot of ovoid pearl shape (Plate 15) is a masterpiece by Shao, and Chen Yongqing's successful handling of massive shapes and proficiency in calligraphy can be reflected by his large teapot with openwork knob (Plate 13). A five-verse poem and the signature of his name are carved on the body in simplified cursive script. Cheng Yuncong was a contemporary of Chen and was noted for his segmented wares. The teapot of sweet osmanthus shape (Plate 16) is one of his representative pieces. One special feature of this teapot is the design of the handle, with the middle figure rest on the underside but without the thumb rest.

Another famous potter active during the late Ming period was Chen Ziqi, the father of Chen Mingyuan, a master potter of the early Qing period. Chen was skilful in modelling ancient bronzes and in the imitation of nature, as reflected by the brushpot in tree trunk form decorated with gardenia branch in relief (Plate 10), which is a common object for the scholar's table.

Hui Mengchen was another prolific potter active at the end of the Ming dynasty. He created one of the most distinctive styles of teapot at Yixing, inscribed with proficient calligraphy. Noted for his miniature teapots of simple design and delicate workmanship, his pieces were widely copied since the Yongzheng period (1723–1736) of the Qing dynasty. Such small teapots are commonly known as Mengchen teapots (Plate 29). They are ideal miniature teapots for brewing *gongfu* tea since the Qing dynasty and are still a favourite of tea lovers of Chaozhou, who prefer to brew Tieguanyin, a kind of Oolong tea, with the use of Mengchen teapots.

Hui Yigong was famous for producing teapots of small size during the first half of the eighteenth century. Plate 30 is a small yellow clay teapot of persimmon fruit shape with the signature "Yigong jianzhi" carved on the base in very elegant running script. It is very thinly potted and is an ideal pot for *gongfu* tea connoisseurs.

Chen Mingyuan[20] has been referred to as one of the most gifted Yixing potters after Shi Dabin. He was well known for his technical virtuosity and creativity, and was particularly famous for his teapots in the naturalistic style. His teapot of melon shape with swirling pattern in relief (Plate 18) illustrates his gentle but refined treatment of segmented wares. On the other hand, the brush rest ingeniously fashioned in the shape of prunus branch (Plate 19) reflects his spectacular ability. The group of various types of fruits and nuts (Plates 20–25) (*Fig. 11*) is very realistically modelled and close in texture and weight to their models.

Fig. 11 Fruits and nuts by
Chen Mingyuan

The tradition of Yixing wares commissioned by the imperial family began in the Ming dynasty but all the ordered pieces at that time are the so-called dragon basins. It was only during the Kangxi reign (1662–1722) and subsequent eras of the Qing dynasty that purple clay teapots were known at the Qing court. The Palace had an interest in collecting deocrative pieces, and purple clay wares with glazing can be dated to the early years of Yongzheng period (1723–35). The glaze was fired at a low temperature of 800–850°C and the application of glaze is under the influence of the *fencai* or *famille-rose* decoration on products at Jingdezhen. However, this kind of glazed works concealed the natural texture of purple clay wares.

As seen from the K.S. Lo Collection, decorative works which are glazed (Plates 33, 34), lacquered (Plate 35), slip decorated (Plates 41, 52) and other enamelled pieces (Plates 50, 53, 54, 64) as well as items applied with relief elements (Plates 31, 36, 38, 39, 103, 108) which greatly inspired the Europeans (Plates 109, 110, 111, 112, 113) were produced during the eighteenth and early nineteenth centuries. Such decorative pieces often give a sense of folk art.

Some members of the imperial family also commissioned Yixing teapots. There is one teapot in the K.S. Lo Collection which is modelled after the square *hu* shape of the Han dynasty (Plate 32). It was ordered by Yunli, the seventeenth son of Emperor Kangxi (reign 1662–1722) and the craftsmanship is simple but superb. The 1849-dated teapot of gourd shape (Plate 50) was made for the owner of Xingyouheng Tang, which was the studio name of Zaiquan or Prince Ding, a royal clansman of the Daoguang period (1821–1850).

Snuff bottles were also produced at Yixing during the late Qing period. Some are decorated in a buff slip with flower and landscape designs on each side (Plate 52); others are finely painted in enamels with landscape scenes (Plates 53, 54).

Patronage by scholars and literary collaboration

From the beginning of the nineteenth century, the production of Yixing wares was closely associated with literati taste because of the patronage by famous scholars. This in turn resulted in a revolution of style with the creation of many simple shaped tea wares on which the scholars could show off their literary talents through painting, calligraphy and seal engraving. Inscriptions are commonly found on the body of teapots made during this period for poetic and religious expression by the literati potters in collaboration with scholars. They are sometimes verses, old sayings, surnames and names of the potters, or titles of their halls, pavilions and studios. The styles of calligraphy are various, but generally they are written in clerical, running and cursive styles and occasionally in the seal and regular scripts (Plates 46–50, 56, 57, 60, 63, 68, 69, 71, 72, 80, 81, 82, 83, 85, 88). The inscriptions were carved by a bamboo knife on the half-dried, leather-hard surface before firing (Fig. 12).

Fig. 12 Inscribing a teapot

The most outstanding representative of the patrons was Chen Hongshou, alias Mansheng.[21] He is recorded as having designed eighteen teapot styles when he served as Magistrate of Liyang,[22] and he commissioned the two leading potters of the time, Yang Pengnian[23] and Shao Erquan[24], to make teapots. The teapots of simple shape with the seal mark "Pengnian" under the handle, "Amantuo Shi" (name of Chen Mansheng's studio) on the base, and decorated with the poetry and signature of Chen Mansheng on the body, are known as "Mansheng teapots". They were highly sought after by Yixing ware collectors because of their artistic value enhanced by literature, calligraphy, seal-carving and pottery. Existing teapots attributed to Chen Mansheng are of simple shapes, with plenty of smooth surfaces for engraving (Plates 46, 47). The teapot of chamfered low cylindrical shape in the K.S. Lo Collection (Plate 46) is marked with fifteen names of Chen's friends including Jiang Tingxiang, Qian Shumei, Shen Chunluo and Lu Xingqing, who assisted in the critical examination of the pot when having a tea gathering at Chen's home. Mansheng teapots not only owe their artistic features to craftsmanship, calligraphy and literature, but also to the overall design of the work. This collaboration between scholars and potters succeeded in producing some of the most charming Yixing pieces.

After Chen Hongshou set the example, famous literati like Qiao Zhongxi[25], Wu Dacheng[26] and others commissioned Yixing teapots (Plates 49, 82). They were responsible for transplanting the folk art of Yixing pottery into literati circles.

Another literary collaborator who was proficient in bamboo painting and frequently applied bamboo and inscriptions on Yixing teapots was Qu Ziye[27]. There are several pieces of such teapots in the K.S. Lo Collection (Plates 48, 57). Unlike Chen Mansheng who only applied calligraphy on the teapot surface, Qu also engraved his expertise prunus or bamboo paintings on them, although sometimes the engravings are a bit superfluous.

An important potter of the Daoguang (1821–50) and Xianfeng (1851–61) periods was Shao Daheng, who was as famous as Yang Pengnian. Whereas Yang was proficient in delicate craftsmanship, Shao excelled in simplicity and dignity of style. Among his representative works, the teapot of bulging round shape (Plate 58) clearly illustrates his clear-cut and simple approach in designing teapots. His another famous piece in the K.S. Lo Collection is the teapot with the decoration of a fish metamorphosing into a dragon (Plate 59). An interesting characteristic of this design is that the tongue of the dragon will stretch out when pouring tea.

Teapots encased in pewter
During the late Qing period, Zhu Jian (alias Shimei), an connoisseur skilled in painting figures and flowers, first combined pewter and jade with purple clay in the making of Yixing teapots. He started the fashion of encasing purple clay teapots in pewter, then engraving the metal surface with calligraphy. These pewter-encased teapots were further embellished with jade knobs and spouts, and handles of jade or silver inlaid hardwood. Plates 43, 44 and 45 are

three examples of his innovated teapots. Some were made by Yang Pengnian (Plates 44, 45) who would add a little square of clay to the interior of the teapot on which he stamped his seal (refer to *Figs 9, 10*). Apart from pewter, sometimes brass and copper mounts are also found in Yixing teapots of the nineteenth century (Plate 66).

Commercial production

Due to the rapid development of the purple clay industry and the expansion of export items, companies were established in Shanghai, Yixing, Wuxi, Tianjin and Hangzhou by industralists during the nineteenth century. These shops commissioned wares from Yixing, but each had its own artists to decorate them. Decorations continued the nineteenth-century style, which combined images from painting and calligraphy.

One of the companies in Shanghai which was established in the second half of the nineteenth century was Tiehua Xuan, which still exists today. Mainly dealing in Yixing wares to Europe, Japan, and Southeast Asia, it owned its own kilns at Yixing. Tiehua Xuan produced items noted for the excellence of their calligraphic decoration. Its shop mark, "Tiehua Xuan zhi", carved in seal script, is enclosed by either a rectangle or a square (Plates 71, 88). Potters who supplied unfired green ware to Tiehua Xuan for further decoration include Jiang Yanting (Plate 88), Chen Guangming (Plate 68), Fan Dasheng (Plate 74), Wang Yinchun (Plates 76, 77) and Cheng Shouzhen (Plates 83, 84). The workmen of the shop would then engrave and further decorate the pieces, and stamp them with the shop's seal.[28]

Other better-known companies during the late nineteenth century and the first half of the twentieth century include Zhen Ji and Wu Desheng. There is one teapot of globular shape produced for Zhen Ji by Shao Youlan in the K.S. Lo Collection (Plates 60). Another teapot with engravings through allover black slip produced for the Wu Company was made by Wu Yaoting, the chief potter (Plate 81). It was inscribed by Qitao (Wu Hanwen) and was made by the luting method in 1922.

Export items

Yixing tea wares were introduced to foreign countries in the seventeenth century with the first consignment of tea and were commonly known as "boccaro" or "Porcelain Rouge".[29] The market for this type of teapots expanded so rapidly by the end of the seventeenth century that even European ceramic factories began to produce imitations to meet the domestic demand.

Yixing pottery was extensively copied in Europe by the Elers Brothers in Staffordshire and others such as Böttger in Meissen. The tankard in red clay (Plate 109) and the teapot with appliqué decoration (Plate 110) are English imitations of Yixing ware. About 1680, the Dutch potter Ary de Milde made a number of pots in imitation of Yixing export pieces (Plates 111, 112). His example was followed later in Meissen (Plate 113).[30]

Early export Yixing wares were mainly made of red clay and decorated with appliqué motifs in the form of twigs of prunus spray or auspicious subjects with a lion knob on the cover (Plates 101, 102, 104, 108). In many cases, the decorations were created by cast moulding or with press moulds or stamps. The teapots were very often enhanced with silver mounting by local silversmiths (Plates 101, 103).

The Nanking Cargo

In 1985, enormous quantities of mid-eighteenth-century ceramics were found on board a Dutch sunken vessel, the Geldermalsen, which were destined for western markets. The ceramics have been known as "Nanking" or "Nankeen" since they began to appear in trade advertisements and auction catalogues in European countries since the 1760s. Western wholesalers and retailers incorrectly believed that these fine ceramics for the export trade were made at Nanking instead of the pottery town of Jingdezhen in Jiangxi province. Thus during the auction at Amsterdam in 1986, the cargo pieces were named "The Nanking Cargo".

Among the cargo, there are eight Yixing teapots, all of which are dated circa 1750 and can be used as a basis for further research on export wares. Dr K.S. Lo acquired half of these pieces and donated them to the Hong Kong Museum of Art. Plates 104 and 105 show two of them: one large teapot of hexagonal shape with a lion finial and a small Mengchen teapot of pear shape with the signature "Yuxiang Zhai" on the base. Both of them reflect the taste of the European markets and the popularity of tea-drinking in Europe, with the use of purple clay teapots as well as blue-and-white porcelain pieces, during the mid-eighteenth century.

Teapots for Thailand

Yixing teapots were introduced to Thailand as early as the Ming dynasty. Increased numbers were exported during the Qing period. They were characterized by their globular, cylindrical or pear-shaped bodies, and design of metal overhead handles and glossy polished surfaces. The spout, lid and knob were embellished with metal rims (Plates 114–118). Many of these were small pots manufactured for brewing *gongfu* tea by local Chinese. Besides, traditional forms of Yixing pots were also imported into Thailand. One of them is the teapot with bamboo motif and braided overhead handle with the stamped mark of Rongqing (Plate 70). The most prominent example was a group of teapots commissioned by King Rama V in 1907 (Plate 117).

Contemporary development of Yixing pottery

Due to the outbreak of the Second World War, the production of Yixing pottery ceased until 1953. During these early years, all the products were stamped with the seal "Zhongguo Yixing (Yixing, China)" instead of carrying on the major feature of Ming and Qing pieces. All the works are made in mass production without inserting the identity of the individual potters. However, the old tradition of adding the potter's seal mark on their works was advocated by ardent connoisseurs like Dr K.S. Lo and finally resumed in 1970s. Several pieces of contemporary works are selected from the K.S. Lo Collection (Plates 89–100) which illustrate the continuity of the purple clay production in China. These contemporary potters have added modern techniques and new shapes to the repertoire of Yixing wares. The tradition of collaboration between scholars, artists and potters (Plates 89, 98) has also continued in recent years under the patronage of Dr K.S. Lo.[31]

Notes

1 Dr K.S. Lo has written the first detailed monograph devoted to Yixing wares entitled *The Stonewares of Yixing : From the Ming period to the present day*, printed by the Sotheby's Publications and Hong Kong University Press in 1986.

2 In ancient times this region was known as Jingxi. After the unification of China by Qin Shihuang in 221 B.C., it was re-named Yangxian. The name Yixing has been used since the Song dynasty (960–1279).

3 The pottery town of Yixing county was named Dingshuzhen in 1950 after the two hills, Dingshan and Shushan, where purple clay was first found.

4 For a detailed survey of the composition of purple clay, please refer to Ye Nonggeng, Li Changhong and Xu Xiutang, "Microscopic Structure and Production Techniques of Purple Clay Wares – An Abstract", in *Innovations in Contemporary Yixing Pottery*, (exhibition catalogue, Hong Kong Museum of Art, 1988), pp. 51–53.

5 Round vessels are produced by the paddling technique with the help of tools such as wooden mallet, sheet cutter, gauge, spatula and bamboo scraper.

6 The luting method is used to produce vessels in square or geometric shapes with flat facets. Tools used include iron cutter, spatula and horn scraper.

7   Ip Wing Chi, "Development in Yixing Pottery", in *Innovations in Contemporary Yixing Pottery*, p. 42 stated that there is "the use of industrial chemicals like cobalt oxide and manganese dioxide to form new clay colours" such as inky green and blackish purple.

8   The dragon kiln was first used by ancient potters in South China. From the Jin dynasty (265–420) onwards, it gradually replaced the round kilns which had been in use since Neolithic times. As the dragon kiln is said to have been founded in Yixing, it is also known as the "Yixing kiln".

9   Cf. the discovery in 1976 of a dragon kiln dated to the Song dynasty and numerous sherds of tea vessels in Yangjiaoshan. See "Survey on the ancient kiln site of Yangjiaoshan in Yixing", *Zhongguo gudai yaozhi diaocha fajue baogao ji*, (Beijing, 1984), pp. 59–63.

10 See the opening paragraph of the Qing treatise *Yangxian mingtao lu* by Wu Xian, in *Taoci pulu*, vol. 2, quoted from Zhou Gaoqi's *Yangxian minghu xi*. This late Ming work is the earliest record on Yixing ware with detailed analysis of its art, characteristics, extant works and potters' biographies.

11 The site of the Jinsha Temple is found in Wufu, about three miles southwest of Dingshuzhen in Yixing county.

12 *Zi* Kexue, *hao* Yishan, Wu Shi was a native of Yixing and was once posted as Administration Vice Commissioner of Sichuan province.

13 See the description on the characteristic of Gongchun's works in *Yangxian minghu xi* by Zhou Gaoqi.

14 Illustrations of two Yongle-dated teapots of this shape can be found in *Porcelain of the National Palace Museum: Blue and White Ware of the Ming Dynasty*, (Hong Kong, 1963), Book 1, plates 18, 18a, 18b & 18c; *Monochrome Ware of the Ming Dynasty*, (Hong Kong, 1968), Book 1, plates 2, 2a & 2b.

15 The other three of the four great Wanli Masters are Dong Han, Zhao Liang and Yuan Chang.

16 The name of the shape was taken from the caps worn by Tibetan monks. It was a popular shape of porcelain during the Yongle period of the Ming dynasty.

17 Xiang Yuanbian (1525–1590), *zi* Zijing, *hao* Molin Jushi, was a native of Jiaxing, Zhejiang province. He was a renowned collector and art connoisseur of the Ming dynasty.

18 Several teapots of Shi Dabin have been excavated from late Ming tombs : the earliest one is a teapot with overhead handle excavated from a 1533-dated tomb of Wu Jing, a eunuch of the Ming dynasty in Nanjing; the second teapot of hexagonal shape which is finely wrought is found from a 1616-dated tomb in Jiangdu near Yangzhou, a third small globular teapot with three legs and loop handle from a 1629-dated tomb in Wuxi, the cover of which is elegantly covered with moulded motifs of clouds. Another teapot of compressed round shape is found in Wuxi; whereas the fourth is found from a 1612-dated tomb in Fujian province and the fifth from a 1639-dated tomb in Yanan. All these teapots are common in their dignified, simple and vigorous style, which tallies with the description of Shi's works in literary sketches of the Ming and Qing dynasties. See Lü Chenglong, "Purple clay teapots with signature of Dabin excavated from Yanan", in *Wenwu tiandi*, 1993, v. 1, pp. 30 – 32.

19 *Zi* Zhongchun and Meigong, *hao* Migong, Chen Jiru (1558–1639) was a native of Huating (present day Songjiang region of Shanghai). A contemporary of the famous artist Dong Qichang, he was also a renowned scholar and prolific writer. He advocated tea-drinking in small teapots together with his friends. He lived as a recluse and excelled in painting and calligraphy.

20 Chen Yuan (active mid 17th to early 18th century), *zi* Mingyuan, *hao* Hefeng, Hecun etc., was a native of Yixing. He was a talented potter who also excelled in calligraphy.

21 Better known as Chen Mansheng (1768–1822), *zi* Zigong, *hao* Mansheng, Mangong, Zhongyu Daoren etc., Chen was a scholar, artist and expert seal carver, and one of the Eight Masters of Xiling.

22 Liyang is a neighbouring county of Yixing in Jiangsu province.

23 Yang Pengnian (1796–1820) came from a family of potters. His brother and sister, Baonian and Fengnian, also made pots for Chen Mansheng.

24 Shao Erquan (active mid 19th century) was both a prolific potter and inscriber.

25 Qiao Zhongxi (active early 19th century), *zi* Luzhou, *hao* Yiyuan, was a distinguished calligrapher and accomplished essayist. As a contemporary of Chen Mansheng and Qu Yingshao, he was also a keen gardener.

26 Wu Dacheng (1835–1902), *zi* Qingqing, *hao* Hengxuan and Kezhai, was a native of Wuxian, Jiangsu province. In 1868 he was appointed as Inspector General of Guangdong and Hunan provinces and was an outstanding calligrapher, excelling in seal script.

27 Qu Yingshao (1780–1849), *zi* Ziye, *hao* Laoye, Hugong Yefu, Ji'an and Xiaogu etc., was a native of Shanghai. A prolific painter and seal-carver, he carried out the decoration of his favourite teapots.

28 For further information of Tiehua Xuan, consult Terese Tse Bartholomew, "In search of Tiehua Xuan" in *Orientations*, May 1990, pp. 86–93.

29 Boccaro is a Portugal term for Yixing ware, which originally referred to a kind pottery produced by the American Indians. "Porcelain Rouge" is the title of a paper published in 1708 by Böttger of England which discusses Yixing red ware.

30 For a detailed discussion on the influence of Yixing ware in the West, see Donald Rabiner, "Yixing and the West", in *The Art of the Yixing Potter*, (exhibition catalogue, 1990, Hong Kong Museum of Art), pp. 92–105.

31 Six more recent collaborated tea wares are illustrated in *Selected Works of Contemporary Yixing Potters*, (exhibition catalogue, 1994, Hong Kong Museum of Art), plates 2, 10, 11, 19, 32 & 35.

羅桂祥珍藏宜興紫砂陶器

黃燕芳

　　茶具文物館羅桂祥珍藏中國陶瓷茶具，涵蓋領域廣泛，爲研究中國歷代茶具提供一個有系統的基礎。藏品以十六世紀至現代的宜興陶器爲主。雖然，學者對部份古代作品的出處、年代仍有不同的看法，但這些紫砂器物的雅緻和優秀質素是無庸置疑的。羅桂祥博士一向以來對收藏與研究紫砂陶器[1]的熱忱，大大推動了海內外人士欣賞宜興陶藝的風氣。今年欣逢茶具文物館開幕十週年紀念，謹藉這篇介紹羅桂祥珍藏中精選紫砂作品的文章，與各界熱衷藝術茗趣的雅士，分享這份茶情陶雅。

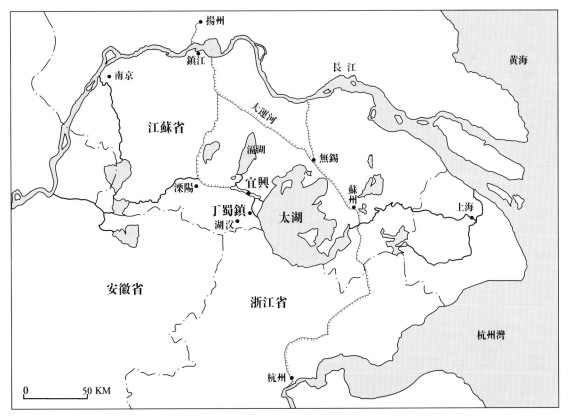

圖一　宜興及其鄰近地區圖

宜興古名荆溪、陽羨[2]，位於江蘇省太湖的西端（圖一），數百年來以製造紫砂陶器而聞名於世，在中國素有「陶都」之稱。

紫砂泥

　　紫砂是生產於宜興南部丘陵山區陶泥的統稱。在宜興南部自丁山至蜀山一帶地區，爲紫砂陶業的集中地，即現今在宜興東南約三十公里的丁蜀鎮所在（圖二）[3]。蜀山出細陶，宜於製作小型茶具；丁山則產粗大陶器，以缸盆之屬見稱。

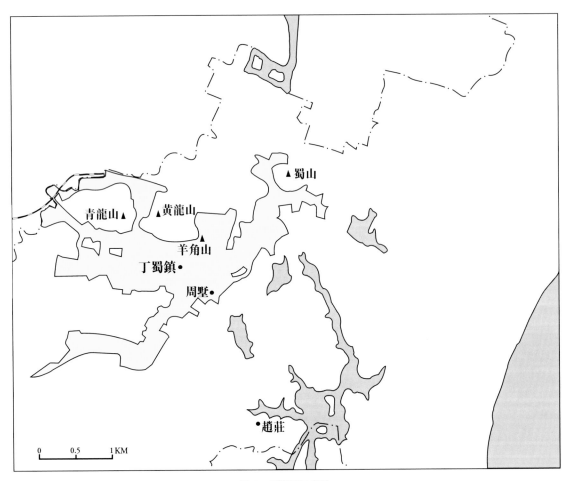

圖二　丁蜀鎮示意圖

紫砂陶泥土質細緻，泥坯韌度極高，含鐵量超過百分之九，而且可塑性佳，乾燥後收縮率較小，產品不易變形，宜於製作精巧的茶壺[4]。由於紫砂泥是一種不能用水直接調稀的陶土，所以不適合以輪製法或注漿法成形，而是需要用手捏造成各類器物。宜興工藝師進一步發展出一套「打身筒」[5]和「鑲身筒」[6]的成型技法，方便製作，並配合創造了以竹、木、牛角和金屬等多種物料製成的專用工具（*圖三*），一直沿用至今。

　　紫砂陶土以攝氏約一千二百度燒成後，有較強的吸水率和較大的氣孔率，所以製成的茗壺都具有良好的吸附和透氣性能。大部份的宜興茶壺素身無飾，只是單看外形和表面紋理已深具美感，淳樸大方，別具風格。原因是在於素淨的器物表裡保留了泥質的吸附氣味性能，泡茶時更能充份發揮茶的香味。此外，使用經年、日加擦拭的紫砂茶壺，表面會泛出一層光澤，形成瑩潤的「包漿」，令人愛不釋手；內壁則日久積聚成一層茶漬，泡茶後茶味更為醇厚。

　　紫砂泥料主要分為紫泥、朱泥（紅泥）和本山綠泥（又名段泥）三種（*圖四*），而以紫泥為主，通稱為紫砂。三種泥料均可單獨用來製作各種器皿，又能互相摻合，或加入礦物顏色，便可得到一系列不同深淺的褐色、紅色和黃褐色調；墨綠色和黑紫色是二十世紀的新色系[7]。

圖三　製作紫砂陶器所用工具。由左至右：明針、旁皮刀、規車、木轉輪、木搭子、不同大小拍板。

圖四　紅泥、紫泥及本山綠泥原料（左）和製成品（右）

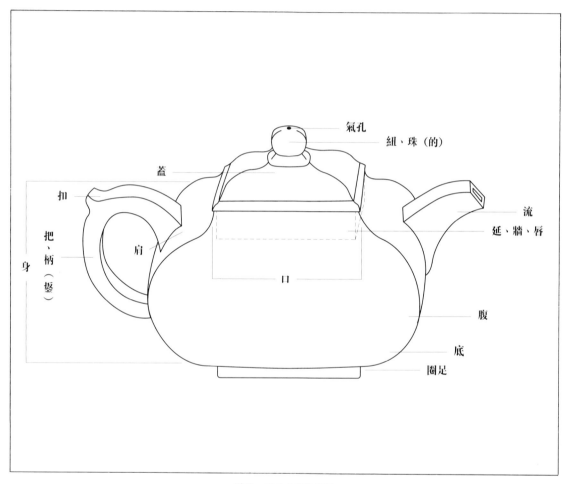

圖中標示：氣孔、紐、珠（的）、蓋、扣、把、柄（鋬）、肩、身、口、流、延、牆、唇、腹、底、圈足

圖五　壺的各部份名稱

宜興陶器的特色

　　宜興陶器素以手藝精巧、造型獨特和泥色優雅見稱。除了器物本身的藝術價值外，也有實際的應用功能，其中紫砂製作的茶壺更被譽爲泡茶妙器。雖然紫砂製品以茗壺最常見和爲人樂用（*圖五*），但宜興也有製作文人的案頭文房用品，見於羅桂祥珍藏的有印泥盒（圖版9）、筆筒（圖版10，14）、筆山（圖版19）、調色盒（圖版88）、水注（圖版95）和其他雜項，如陶塑（圖版92，94）和一對紫砂陶枕（圖版69）等。

　　在紫砂造型方面，大致可分爲幾何形、仿自然物體和筋紋器幾種。

幾何形是紫砂茶壺中最爲普遍採用的型制，主要是從球體、圓柱體、方棱柱體和其他幾何形狀衍變成形。羅桂祥珍藏中有不少這類器物（圖版1，7，11，15，17，26，32，33，34，41，42，46，48，49，56，57，58，60，62，63，71，73，76－86，97，99，114－118）。這些光身（普遍稱爲光貨）或部份加飾刻銘的幾何形作品造型簡潔優雅，深受茗家歡迎。這類型制的另一特色是各式提梁的設計，大大增加外觀的雅緻（圖版27，37，67，68，89，98）。

仿自然物體器物題材包括樹幹、植物和各種花卉型制。這類富於裝飾性的器物最宜於陶藝家發揮他們的想像力和對大自然敏銳的觀察力。羅桂祥珍藏中有不少這類仿自然物體作品，俗稱花貨。花貨中最受歡迎的題材是歲寒三友的松、竹、梅，如松幹浮雕筆筒（圖版14）；以竹爲型制或裝飾的作品爲數不少（圖版12，28，48，49，56，57，70，72，88，100），而以梅枝或梅花爲題材或裝飾的器物也有數件（圖版19，39，50，108）。其中最具代表性的創作包括陳鳴遠的梅枝形筆山（圖版19）、陳仲美的束竹柴圓壺（圖版12）、范錦甫的巧色佛手壺（圖版87）、蔣蓉的土狗樹蛙水注（圖版95）和汪寅仙的翠鳥蓮蓬壺（圖版96）。這些作品形象生動，充份表現出陶人的精湛工藝和對於大自然的深刻體會。

筋紋器主要包括那些模仿各式花卉和帶瓜棱的植物瓜果形器物。筋紋器要求精確的設計和處理自然花果造型技藝的掌握，作品具有節奏感。羅桂祥珍藏中有不少花卉形的筋瓢壺，題材有水仙花（圖版2）、玉蘭花（圖版3）、菊花（圖版6）和桂花（圖版16）。這些作品對於壺身和壺蓋的接合有很嚴格的要求，口蓋準縫既緊密而又通轉的才是上品。

宜興陶器裝飾手法多樣化，有在器身上加上泥繪，即以化粧土繪畫紋飾（圖版41，52），也有在器身上施滿爐均釉（圖版33, 34）或貼花（圖版10，14，87，95，96，100），與及有鏤空紋飾的作品（圖版28）；有些十八世紀的宜興器物上更飾以粉彩（圖版40，50，53，54，64，107）。泥繪和彩飾都是陶藝家力求製造顏色對比效果的裝飾手法。

此外，宜興藝人又借鑒古代青銅器（圖版8，36）和漢碑（圖版43）等造型而翻陳出新。當代宜興陶藝家更創製以銀片或銀絲鑲嵌紫砂壺（圖版99），作品色澤對比鮮明。這種裝飾手法始見於中國古代青銅器，當代陶藝家利用傳統技法而加以創新。

圖六　程壽珍掇球壺(圖版84)　　　圖七　顧紹培高風亮節壺(圖版100)　　　圖八　圖版117，118蓋延上泰文印
　　　　印款位置圖　　　　　　　　　　　　　印款位置圖

　　宜興陶器的一大特色是帶有作者印款。所有紫砂器具都
有作者款識，甚或同時蓋上壺手、銘刻者和設計者的印章
（圖版46）。鐫印或刻款所在之處，或在壺底，或在流下，
或在把上或下方，或在蓋裡（*圖六、圖七*），或蓋之外口
（*圖八*）；在特別情況下，如圖版44和45的包錫壺，印章
更蓋於壺內底部中央（*圖九、圖十*）。至於書體方面，大抵
明代作品以楷書為主（圖版1-5，7-9，11-14），其後
則有行草款，並以篆刻印章最大行其道。這些款識或是姓
名，或是別號，或是詩句，或是堂館閣齋諸號，循此可以追
溯壺手和銘刻家身份，及提供生產地點和創作年代的佐證資
料。

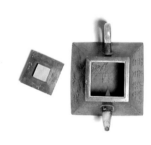

圖九　圖版44壺內底部印款

　　作者署款的傳統是中國陶瓷史上的一個特例，顯示出側
重個人表現、強調個人風格的特點。此外，這種安排也肯定
了作品的價值和陶人的社會地位，成為有關紫砂陶器最可靠
的背景資料。

圖十　圖版45壺內底部印款

紫砂陶器的發展

　　茶具文物館的基本藏品中，宜興陶器佔了半數，它們以簡單質樸的造型和富於藝術和
實用價值而聞名寰宇。過去三百年來，宜興陶業的長足發展，實有賴明清兩代文人學者的
積極參與和提倡。

紫砂陶器的製作，實在遠早於明代。一九七六年宜興羊角山發現的宋代（九六〇至一一二五年）紫砂龍窰[8]和紫砂殘器碎片，被視為明清兩代紫砂器的濫觴[9]。可是，紫砂器創作自明代中期開始，一直蓬勃至今，其中的客觀原因，是飲茶方法的轉變，由煮茶末改為沏茶葉。基於泡茶法流行，所以透氣性強、能耐高溫的茶壺便應運而生。宜興紫砂由於泥質的特點，更加獨擅勝場，紫砂茶壺遂大受各界愛好茗飲人士歡迎。

　　紫砂陶泥的發現，傳說與一位異僧有關。相傳有一天異僧到村中，「呼曰：賣富貴；土人群嗤之。僧曰：貴不欲買，買富何如？因引邨叟指山中產土之穴，及去發之，果備五色，爛若披錦[10]」。羅桂祥珍藏中有這個始陶異僧的雕像，手持五色泥，是當代紫砂名家徐秀棠的作品（圖版92）。

　　紫砂壺一般都認為源出金沙寺[11]老僧和正德年間（一五〇六至一五二一年）進士吳頤山[12]的書僮供春。吳氏在金沙寺中讀書準備赴考，供春偶然窺見寺中老僧製造陶壺，而仿製了一把狀如樹癭的紫砂壺。羅桂祥珍藏中便有一個晚清著名壺手黃玉麟仿製的「供春壺」（圖版61）。黃氏擅長仿古，特別是傳統的供春壺式。據明人記載供春的作品特點是「栗色闇闇，如古金鐵[13]」。一個造型簡潔，底有「大明正德八年（1513）供春」楷書刻款的圓囊壺是羅桂祥珍藏中紀年最早的作品（圖版1）。壺身淺雕六瓣，外形模仿永樂年間景德鎮製作的瓷壺[14]；壺肩可見接合痕跡，可知壺身是上下兩部分合製而成，為早期砂壺的特色。金沙寺僧和供春可說是將紫砂陶器專業化和藝術化的開創者。

　　晚明的另一著名壺手是時鵬，有關時鵬的資料不多，只知他是活躍於萬曆年間（一五七三至一六二〇年）陶壺四名家之一[15]。羅桂祥珍藏中的水仙花形方壺（圖版2），底有「時鵬」二字刻款，造型精巧中見古樸，壺身與壺蓋接合天衣無縫，把上平肩處的扣，設計獨特，方便持壺奉茶。

　　時大彬是時鵬之子，供春弟子，生於明萬曆年間，卒於清康熙初年，是明末清初最著名的壺藝大家。明清筆記中都記述他為人敦雅古穆，製作態度十分認真，「遇不愜意碎之」，因此存世作品極少。羅桂祥珍藏中有數件時大彬作品，其中的蓮瓣僧帽壺（圖版4），前屬倫敦戴維德爵士藏品，型制借鑑於元代的西藏注子器形[16]。時氏其他傑作包括玉蘭花六瓣壺（圖版3）和印包方壺（圖版5），後者底部有「墨林堂」刻款，說明是明代著

名鑑藏家項元汴[17]所訂製。近年明墓中出土了不少時大彬的茶壺，特點都是端莊渾厚，古樸雅緻[18]。時氏早期作品多仿供春大壺，以樸雅堅致見長；後期由於和陳繼儒[19]等文人交往，遂改製小壺。這標誌著紫砂壺藝和文人士大夫品味相結合的肇端。

李茂林也是活躍於萬曆年間的陶匠，一般稱他為李養心，所製砂壺研麗樸緻兼而有之。配以如意紋足的菊花八瓣壺（圖版6）可說是他的代表作品。李氏長子李仲芳是時大彬的得意門生，所製觚稜壺（圖版7）型制仿古中見新意，造工文巧。

徐友泉也是萬曆年間的製壺名手，對泥色配製和茗壺造型，多有創新；又擅長仿製古代青銅器形，如盉形三足壺（圖版8）便是一例。陳仲美是另一位活躍於晚明的陶人，祖藉江西婺源。他在萬曆年間於景德鎮造瓷，後棄業至宜興從事砂壺創作，所造茗壺文玩極工細有趣，如束竹柴圓壺（圖版12）便是他的代表作，其中一節竹稍高出於蓋面成蓋鈕，設計巧妙，無邊緣痕跡。

同時活躍於萬曆年間的還有邵文銀和陳用卿兩位陶工。前者的素身圓珠壺（圖版15）外形簡單中見精緻，後者所造的弦紋刻銘大壺（圖版13），充份反映陳氏處理渾圓豐滿造型的技巧和精湛的書藝，壺身以嫻熟的章草刀法刻上五言詩及名款：「詩人吟白雪，才子步青雲。用卿。」與陳用卿同時的承雲從，則擅長筋紋器類，如桂花四瓣壺（圖版16）便是他的典型作品，最特別是其把扣的設計不用以攔拇指，而是安排在把下方作承托中指之用。

另一位活躍於晚明的壺手是陳子畦，他是清初陶藝大家陳鳴遠的父親，精於仿古和模仿自然生趣，其樹段筆筒（圖版10）上有不同色泥的梔子花裝飾，是富於文人雅趣的案頭用品。

惠孟臣是明末的一位多產陶藝家。他製壺注重銘刻書法，擅製簡樸而精工的小壺，胎薄輕巧，在清初雍正年間已有人仿製。後人尊稱這類薄胎小壺為「孟臣壺」（圖版29）。這類小壺最宜於沖泡功夫茶，至今仍是潮汕茗家樂於採用的茶具。

到了十八世紀上半葉，惠逸公是另一位擅長製作小壺的陶工。圖版30的圓腹小壺刻有優美行書底款，署以「逸公監製」，胎質細薄，是沖泡功夫茶的上選茶壺。

陳鳴遠[20]是時大彬以後最傑出的宜興陶人。他的作品以技巧和創意見稱，特別擅長製作像生一類茶壺，從漩渦紋瓜形壺（圖版18）可見其處理筋紋器的獨特手法。陳氏多才多藝，所作的梅枝形筆山（圖版19）和清供果仁小品（圖版20－25）（*圖十一*），都栩栩如生，迫肖實物，後者更是在祀堂廟宇長年供奉的理想祭品。

圖十一 陳鳴遠作清供果仁

宜興陶器內貢宮廷始於明代，當時上貢品種主要是龍缸。康熙朝（一六六二至一七二二年）以後紫砂壺才引入宮廷。皇室用品追求富麗堂皇的習尚，也影響了紫砂陶器的裝飾風格。約在雍正年間（一七二三至一七三五年）起，紫砂產品中出現掛釉器，所施釉料都以攝氏八百至八百五十度低溫燒成。這種彩釉的裝飾手法源自景德鎮的粉彩技術，但卻令紫砂器失去了光身時的自然風格。

在十八世紀和十九世紀初期，宜興生產了不少帶釉的器物（圖版33，34）。在羅桂祥珍藏中，其他富於裝飾性的品種有仿漆器剔紅夔龍紋壺（圖版35）、泥繪茗壺和鼻煙壺（圖版41，52）、各式彩釉器（圖版50，53，54，64），及貼花或淺浮雕裝飾的器物（圖版31，36，38，39，103，108）。後二者的裝飾手法常在外國仿宜興作品中採用（圖版109，110，111，112，113），這類彩釉或加飾器物通常帶有濃厚的民間工藝色彩。

不少皇室中人都有訂製賞玩紫砂茶壺。羅桂祥珍藏中的一個仿漢代方壺造型的茗壺（圖版32），便是由康熙皇帝的第十七子允禮所訂製，造工簡潔精巧。圖版50的粉彩梅枝刻銘壺，是為行有恒堂主人而製作，乃道光年間（一八二一至一八五零年）清宗室載銓清賞之物。

宜興在晚清時期也生產鼻煙壺，有些以化粧土飾以米黃山水花卉（圖版52），有些則彩繪山水，畫工精細（圖版53，54）。

文人購藏紫砂壺的風尚和合作茗壺

踏入十九世紀初期，宜興陶藝發展十分蓬勃，這與文人墨客、名門高士的賞玩、推崇和參與創作有很密切的關係。造型簡單而壺身多空間的光身作品大行其道，方便文人雅士在茗壺上發揮他們在書畫篆刻各方面的才情。這時期不少雅流陶工與文人士大夫合作製壺，在壺身刻上詩詞和有宗教意味的銘文，包括詩句古語、陶人姓名字號、與及堂館閣齋諸號。當時銘刻的書體各異，大致上以隸、行、草書爲主，篆、眞體爲副（圖版46—50，56，57，60，63，68，69，71，72，80，81，82，83，85，88）。銘刻家多用竹尖刀或鐵製刀，在坯體未乾前或乾濕合宜時進行鐫刻工作（圖十二）。

圖十二 在壺身上刻銘

最積極參與和推動茶壺創作活動的可算是金石書畫家陳鴻壽[21]，號曼生。相傳陳氏作宰溧陽[22]時，曾設計壺樣十八式，延聘當時名家楊彭年[23]和邵二泉[24]製壺。其中鋬下鈐「彭年」款，底蓋「阿曼陀室（曼生齋名）」印，壺身飾以詩文和陳曼生刻款的茶壺，稱爲「曼生壺」。除了本身藝術性外，這些士人和壺手合作茗壺更有書法、篆刻、詩詞和文學等方面的欣賞價值，因此成爲收藏宜興陶器人士夢寐以求的珍品。現存曼生壺大多造型簡練，壺身飾以刻銘（圖版46，47）。羅桂祥珍藏中的直腹刻銘曼生壺（圖版46），下腹近底部刻上十五個陳氏朋友的名字，包括江聽香、錢淑美、沈春蘿和陸星卿等，證明此壺曾在一雅集中共同品定。曼生壺的藝術特色不單在於壺藝、書法和文學，更重要的還在於有完整的總體設計，儒雅含蓄。由於文人雅士積極推動宜興陶藝，並與當代著名壺手合製了不少絕妙精品，宜興紫砂器的藝術創作於是在短短數百年間成績斐然。

自從陳鴻壽開了巧工名士合作的先河後，不少名士如喬重禧[25]，吳大澂[26]等都曾訂製並賞玩砂壺（圖版49，82），把紫砂陶器從一門民間藝術提升進入文人雅士的領域。

另一個擅長在茗壺上刻畫銘句的書畫篆刻名家是瞿子冶[27]。羅桂祥珍藏中也有數件瞿氏刻竹銘的作品（圖版48，57）。同代陳曼生只在壺身上以書法刻銘，瞿子冶進一步以梅、竹在砂壺上書畫並刻，令壺身紋飾不免過於紛亂。

邵大亨是活躍於道光（一八二一至一八五零年）和咸豐（一八五一至一八六一年）年間的陶藝家，與楊彭年齊名。楊氏以精巧見長，大亨則以渾樸取勝；傳世品中的素身鼓腹壺（圖版58）外形渾重簡潔。另一件著名作品魚化龍壺（圖版59）則設計巧妙，注茶時蓋上龍舌會順勢伸出。

包錫茗壺

晚清鑑賞家朱堅，長於人物花卉畫，將紫砂與錫、玉石互相結合製壺，可謂別出心裁。他創製的砂胎包錫壺，錫面銘刻書畫，蓋鈕、流和把則配以玉石裝飾（圖版43，44，45）。其中由楊彭年製造的兩把壺（圖版44，45），印章蓋於壺內底部中央（參見圖九、圖十），十分罕見。除了錫這種金屬外，在十九世紀也出現了鑲銅的裝飾茶壺（圖版66）。

商業生產

踏入十九世紀，隨著宜興陶業的不斷發展和銷售地區的擴大，不少資本家紛紛在上海和蘇、浙、皖各省大城市如無錫、天津和杭州開行設店。所有的店舖都在宜興訂貨，但各有自己的藝人從事裝飾光貨的工作。裝飾的風格上承十九世紀，以摹刻書畫為主。

鐵畫軒是設在上海的一家售賣紫砂陶器的商號，在十九世紀後期開始生產主要出口歐洲、日本和東南亞，以書法優美見稱的製品，公司印記成方形或長方形（圖版71，88）。供應素坯給鐵畫軒的陶工包括蔣燕亭（圖版88）、陳光明（圖版68）、范大生（圖版74）、王寅春（圖版76，77）和程壽珍（圖版83，84）等。店內陶工會在素坯上加刻紋飾，並蓋上公司印記[28]。

十九世紀末至二十世紀初售賣紫砂器店舖的表表者還有眞記和吳德盛。羅桂祥珍藏中有一個眞記出品，邵友蘭製作的刻銘鼓腹壺（圖版60），另一個由吳德盛公司主要陶工吳耀庭所製的黑陶衣刻花鳥銘方壺（圖版81），是一九二二年由跂陶（吳漢文）所刻，採用鑲身筒的接板方法做成。

外銷商品

紫砂器物流傳到外國，始於十七世紀。明代末年，紫砂製品隨著茶貨的外銷而流行於歐洲。當時的紫砂陶器被稱爲「鉢開羅」，原是美國印第安人的土器名稱，又被譽爲「紅色瓷器」[29]。由於歐洲市場對於紫砂茶壺的需求甚殷，到了十七世紀晚期不少歐洲陶瓷作坊便開始仿製紫砂器，其中一個是斯塔德福郡作坊的埃勒斯兄弟，圖版109和110便是英國仿宜興的貼花直身盃和茶壺。約在一六八〇年，荷蘭陶匠達米爾仿製了不少宜興貼花或加彩茶壺（圖版111，112），其後德國的波格也效法（圖版113）[30]。

早期的外銷紫砂陶器以朱泥爲主，壺身常飾以貼花浮雕梅花或吉祥圖案，蓋上或配以獅鈕（圖版101，102，104，108），大多數紋飾是以印模壓製或拍印而成，歐洲人更常在壺上加添精美金屬配件（圖版101，103）。

南京貨物

一九八五年，潛水員自一艘荷蘭沉船熱德馬森號，成功打撈出數以噸計的十八世紀中葉外銷歐洲的陶瓷器。自一七六〇年代以來，歐洲國家在貿易廣告和拍賣目錄都稱中國外銷瓷器爲「南京」，意指生產地是在中國的南京。這實在是一大謬誤，正確的來源應是江西的景德鎮。在一九八六年阿姆斯特丹的沉船貨物拍賣，仍沿用舊稱，把所有拍賣品稱爲「南京貨物」。

貨物中包括八個紫砂茶壺，由於可以明確知道生產年代約在十八世紀中葉，爲研究外銷紫砂器提供了重要的佐證。羅桂祥博士在拍賣會上成功競投得半數紫砂壺，並慨贈予香港藝術館；圖版104的獸鈕六方壺和圖版105底刻「玉香齋」款的梨形小壺便是其中兩件，代表了外銷歐洲器物的典型，也証明了在十八世紀中葉，歐洲人除了採購青花瓷器外，紫砂器物也在搜羅之列。

外銷泰國茶壺

早在明代，紫砂茶壺已外銷至泰國，到了清代數量更大幅增加。這些外銷泰國茶壺造型有梨形、圓筒形、扁圓形和圓形，配以金屬提梁，器身磨光，而蓋沿、口沿、流尖和蓋鈕都鑲金或其他金屬（圖版114—118）。大部份訂製小壺的都是當地中國人，以用作冲泡功夫茶。外銷器形之中不乏傳統造型，例如帶有「榮卿」印款的提梁竹節壺（圖版70）。但最突出的是泰王拉瑪五世於一九〇七年訂製的鑲金圓壺（圖版117）。

當代宜興陶器的發展

第二次世界大戰爆發，宜興陶業迫於停止生產，直至一九五三年才恢復投產。復業初年，所有紫砂器物上都一式蓋上「中國宜興」印款，一反明清以來的傳統。製成品以行貨為主，缺少陶工的個人風格。幸好在熱心宜興陶藝的人士，特別是羅桂祥博士等有心人大力鼓吹下，終於在一九七〇年代再度恢復每件作品加上作者印款的傳統。是次展覽也自羅桂祥珍藏中挑選出十二件當代宜興名家的代表作品（圖版89—100），以顯示紫砂陶藝的繼承和發展。這些陶藝家的近作無論在造型和技巧方面，都有創新之處。此外，基於羅桂祥博士的鼓勵和支持，以往文人、書畫家、銘刻家和壺手合作製造茗壺的風氣，近年又再度復興（圖版89，98）[31]。

註釋

[1] 羅桂祥博士著作了一本宜興陶器的專著《由明代至現代的宜興炻器》，（蘇富比及香港大學出版社，一九八六）。

[2] 宜興古名荊溪，因荊溪河而得名。公元前二二一年，秦始皇滅楚後，改名陽羨。公元三〇四年晉惠帝更名義興。至北宋因避宋太宗趙光義的名諱，義興改為宜興，沿用迄今。

[3] 一九五〇年丁山至蜀山一帶的紫砂產地和陶業中心被命名為丁蜀鎮。

[4] 有關紫砂泥結構的詳細分析，參閱葉龍耕、李昌鴻、徐秀棠所撰〈宜興紫砂陶的生產工藝特點和顯微結構〉，《紫砂春華：當代宜興陶藝》展覽目錄，（香港藝術館，一九八八），頁44—50。

[5] 紫砂陶器中的圓形器物，是用打身筒方法製成。所利用工具包括木搭子、矩車、規車、木拍子和竹範等。

[6] 鑲身筒方法適用於製造方形的紫砂器物，所用工具有旁皮刀、木拍子及明針等。

[7] 葉榮枝在《紫砂春華》展覽目錄所撰〈紫砂陶發展概述〉一文頁29指出，在一九一六年開始「利用工業化學原料如氧化鈷、氧化錳等配成墨綠泥、黑紫泥等新泥色……。」

[8] 龍窯是中國古代南方陶工開創的陶窯，到了晉代（二六五至四二〇年）時取代了自新石器時期以來沿用的直焰圓窯。由於龍窯據說是宜興首創的，所以又稱「宜興窯」。

9 紫砂窰址位於宜興蠡墅村羊角山，是丁蜀鎮黃龍山的支脈，出土紫砂器殘片年代早至北宋中期，見〈宜興羊角山古窰址調查簡報〉，《中國古代窰址調查發掘報告集》，（北京文物出版社，一九八四），頁59－63。

10 清人吳騫所著《陽羨名陶錄》卷上第一段，見《陶瓷譜錄》下冊，轉載自明末周高起所著《陽羨茗壺系》，此乃最早見於文字記載有關宜興紫砂陶器的專著，對紫砂的工藝、特點、傳器和藝人傳略都有詳細的記述。

11 金沙寺在宜興丁蜀鎮西南八華里的湖汶。

12 吳頤山，名仕，字克學，宜興人，曾官至四川參政。

13 見明末周高起所著《陽羨茗壺系》。

14 永樂瓷壺圖片，可參見《故宮藏瓷：明青花瓷一》，（香港，一九六三），圖十八，十八（甲），十八（乙），十八（丙）；和《故宮藏瓷：明單色釉瓷一》，（香港，一九六八），圖二，圖二（甲），圖二（乙）。

15 萬曆時的陶壺四名家指時鵬、董翰、趙良和元暢。

16 這個器形名稱源出於西藏喇嘛所戴的僧帽，官窯製作瓷質僧帽壺可能始於明代永樂年間。

17 項元汴（一五二五至一五九○年），字子京，號墨林居士，浙江嘉興人，爲明代最有名的鑒賞家和收藏家。

18 自晚明墓葬出土的「大彬」款茶壺，包括：（1）南京明代太監吳經墓紀年1533的紫砂提梁壺，（2）揚州附近江都紀年1616明墓出土六方形執壺，（3）無錫紀年1629墓葬出土雲頭紋蓋鼓腹三足壺及另一出土直流扁圓腹執壺，（4）福建紀年1612墓葬出土的鼎足蓋圓壺和（5）延安紀年1639墓出土的紫砂提梁壺等。見呂成龍，〈延安出土的大彬款紫砂壺〉，〈文物天地〉一九九三年第一號，頁30－32。這些出土大彬款茗壺外形端莊渾厚，樸素無華，與明清文獻所載「不務妍媚，而樸雅堅致，妙不可思」風格相符。

19 陳繼儒（一五五八至一六三九年），字仲醇，一字眉公，號糜公，華亭（今上海市松江）人，與同郡董其昌齊名，工詩文書畫。

20 陳遠（活躍於十七世紀中葉至十八世紀初），字鳴遠，號鶴峰、鶴邨、壺隱等，宜興人，工製各式文玩茗壺，書法雅健，製壺造工精雅。

21 陳鴻壽（一七六八至一八二二年），字子恭，號曼生、曼公、種榆道人等，錢塘（今杭州）人，詩文書畫皆以資勝，又精通篆刻，爲西泠八家之一。

22 溧陽乃宜興鄰縣，地在江蘇省。

23 楊彭年（一七九六至一八二○年）出身製壺世家，其家人楊寶年和楊鳳年也曾爲陳曼生製作茗壺。

24 邵二泉活躍於十九世紀中期，除精於製壺外，還是鐫刻名家。

25 喬重禧（活躍於十九世紀初期），字鷺洲，工書法文賦，與陳鴻壽、瞿應紹同時；精通園藝，別號宜園。

26 吳大澂（一八三五至一九○二年），字清卿，號恆軒、愙齋，江蘇吳縣人。一八六八年任湖南、廣東巡撫，精於書法，尤擅篆書。

27 瞿應紹（一七八○至一八四九年），字子冶，號老冶、壺公冶父、吉安和小谷等，華亭（今上海市）人。子冶長於書畫篆刻，並只在心愛茗壺上刻以書畫。

[28] 有關鐵畫軒的詳細論述，參考謝瑞華，〈鐵畫軒溯源〉，〈東方藝術〉，一九九〇年五月號，頁86－93。

[29] 一七〇八年，英國人波格發表一篇題爲〈紅色瓷器〉的論文，討論宜興朱泥陶器。

[30] 有關宜興紫砂器影響歐洲作坊的詳細論述，參考樂賓納，〈宜興陶器西漸〉，《宜興陶藝》展覽目錄，（香港藝術館，一九九〇），頁106－117。

[31] 羅桂祥博士近年訂製的六個合作茶具，參見《紫砂新品：當代宜興茶具精選》展覽目錄，（香港藝術館，一九九四），圖版2，10，11，19，32和35。

PLATES

1 ——————————————

Teapot of dome shape with six-lobed body
Signature: Gongchun
Dated 8th year of Zhengde period (1513)
H: 9.9 cm   W: 11.8 cm
C81.511

六瓣圓囊壺
「供春」刻款
「大明正德八年」（1513）作
高：9.9厘米　闊：11.8厘米
C81.511

2

Teapot of hexagonal shape with narcissus-like six-lobed shoulder and cover
Signature: Shi Peng
Mid 16th century
H: 9 cm   W:16.8 cm
C81.517

水仙花六瓣方壺
「時鵬」刻款
十六世紀中葉
高：9厘米　闊：16.8厘米
C81.517

3 ─────────────

Teapot of magnolia shape
Signature: Shi Dabin zhi
Dated spring of *ding you* year,
Wanli period (1597)
H: 8 cm　W: 12.1 cm
C81.498

玉蘭花六瓣壺
「時大彬製」刻款
「萬曆丁酉春」（1597）作
高：8厘米　闊：12.1厘米
C81.498

4

Teapot of monk's cap shape with lotus crown
Signature: Shi Dabin zhi
Dated *ding you* year of Wanli period (1597)
H: 9.3 cm   W: 9.4 cm
C81.506

蓮瓣僧帽壺
「時大彬製」刻款
「萬曆丁酉年」（1597）作
高：9.3厘米   闊：9.4厘米
C81.506

5

Teapot in shape of square seal wrapped in cloth
Signature: Molin Tang [Xiang Yuanbian];
[Shi] Dabin
Late 16th century
H: 6.9 cm   W: 7.7 cm
C81.505

印包方壺
「墨林堂（項元汴）（時）大彬」刻款
十六世紀晚期
高：6.9厘米　闊：7.7厘米
C81.505

6 ————————————————

Teapot of multi-lobed chrysanthemum shape
Seal: Li Maolin zao
Late 16th century
H: 9.6 cm　　W: 11.5 cm
C81.518

菊花八瓣壺
「李茂林造」印
十六世紀晚期
高：9.6厘米　　闊：11.5厘米
C81.518

7

Teapot of square shape with curved sides
Signature: [Li] Zhongfang
Late 16th century
H: 7.2 cm   W: 9.2 cm
C81.501

觚稜壺
「（李）仲芳」刻款
十六世紀晚期
高：7.2厘米　闊：9.2厘米
C81.501

8 ─────────────────────

Teapot of ancient *he* vessel shape
Signature: [Xu] Youquan
Early 17th century
H: 12.4 cm   W: 8.2 cm
C81.504

仿古「盉」形三足壺
「（徐）友泉」刻款
十七世紀初期
高：12.4厘米　闊：8.2厘米
C81.504

9

Seal paste box of mythical animal shape
Signature: [Xu] Youquan fang gu
Dated autumn of *wu wu* year (1618)
H: 8.5 cm   W: 12.8 cm
C81.445

異獸印泥盒
「（徐）友泉仿古」刻款
「戊午（1618）秋日」作
高：8.5厘米　闊：12.8厘米
C81.445

10

**Brush pot in tree trunk form decorated
with gardenia branch in relief**
Seal: Chen Ziqi
Second quarter of 17th century
H: 13.4 cm   W: 9.5 cm
C81.455

貼梔子花樹段筆筒
「陳子畦」印
十七世紀上半葉
高：13.4厘米　闊：9.5厘米
C81.455

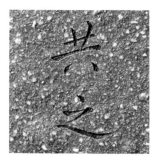

11

Teapot of squat rectangular shape with convex sides
Signature: Gongzhi [Chen Chen]
Early 17th century
H: 7 cm   W: 9.5 cm
C81.510

長方扁壺
「共之（陳辰）」刻款
十七世紀初期
高：7厘米　闊：9.5厘米
C81.510

Teapot in shape of bundled bamboo
Signature: Chen Zhongmei zuo
Dated *gui chou* year of Wanli period (1613)
H: 7.7 cm   W: 9.3 cm
C81.513

束竹柴圓壺
「陳仲美作」刻款
「萬曆癸丑」（1613）作
高：7.7厘米　闊：9.3厘米
C81.513

13

**Large teapot with cloud collar motif on
cover and openwork knob**
Signature: [Chen] Yongqing
1620s
H: 28.6 cm   W: 22 cm
C81.418

弦紋金錢如意壺
「（陳）用卿」刻款
1620年代
高：28.6厘米　闊：22厘米
C81.418

14

**Brush pot decorated with pine tree
in relief**
Signature: Weiqing Laoren
Dated spring of *jia shen* year,
Chongzhen period (1644)
H: 11.8 cm   W: 10 cm
C81.454

松幹浮雕筆筒
「味清老人」刻款
「崇禎甲申（1644）春」作
高：11.8厘米　闊：10厘米
C81.454

15

Teapot of ovoid shape
Seal: Shao Hengyu [Shao Wenyin] *zhi*
Early 17th century
H: 9.6 cm   W: 8.9 cm
C81.499

素身圓珠壺
「邵亨裕（邵文銀）制」印
十七世紀初期
高：9.6厘米　闊：8.9厘米
C81.499

16 ——————————

Teapot of sweet osmanthus shape
Signature: [Cheng] Yuncong zhi,
dedicated to Mr Lüzhong
Second quarter of 17th century
H: 6.7 cm   W: 9.6 cm
C81.509

桂花四瓣壺
「（承）雲從製爲履中先生」刻款
十七世紀上半葉
高：6.7厘米　闊：9.6厘米
C81.509

17

Teapot of flattened round shape
Seal: Cuizhu Ju
Early 18th century
H: 7.7 cm   W: 27.7 cm
C81.404

素身扁圓壺
「翠竹居」印
十八世紀初期
高：7.7厘米　闊：27.7厘米
C81.404

18

Teapot of melon shape with swirling
pattern in relief
Signature: [Chen] Mingyuan
Early 18th century
H: 7.5 cm   W: 10.6 cm
C81.519

漩渦紋瓜形壺

「（陳）鳴遠」刻款

十八世紀初期

高：7.5厘米　闊：10.6厘米

C81.519

19 ————————————————————

Brush rest of prunus branch shape
Seal: Chen Mingyuan
Early 18th century
H: 3.9 cm   W: 14.1 cm
C81.452

梅枝形筆山
「陳鳴遠」印
十八世紀初期
高：3.9厘米　闊：14.1厘米
C81.452

20

Caltrop fruit
Seal: Hecun [Chen Mingyuan]
Early 18th century
H: 3 cm   L: 7.5 cm
C81.462

清供菱角
「鶴邨（陳鳴遠）」印
十八世紀初期
高：3厘米　長：7.5厘米
C81.462

21

Water-chestnut
Seal: [Chen] Mingyuan
Early 18th century
H: 3.5 cm   W: 3.6 cm
C81.466

清供荸薺
「（陳）鳴遠」印
十八世紀初期
高：3.5厘米　闊：3.6厘米
C81.466

22

Walnut
Seal: [Chen] Mingyuan
Early 18th century
H: 4.1 cm   W: 4 cm
C81.465

清供胡桃
「（陳）鳴遠」印
十八世紀初期
高：4.1厘米　闊：4厘米
C81.465

23

Two peanuts
Seals: Chen, Mingyuan, Hecun
Early 18th century
L: 3.6 cm
C81.467 (A, B)

清供花生
「陳」，「鳴遠」及「鶴邨」印
十八世紀初期
長：3.6厘米
C81.467 (A, B)

24

Chestnut
Seal: [Chen] Mingyuan
Early 18th century
L: 3.5 cm   W: 3 cm
C81.464

清供栗子
「（陳）鳴遠」印
十八世紀初期
長：3.5厘米　闊：3厘米
C81.464

25

Arrowroot
Seals: Chen, Mingyuan
Early 18th century
L: 6.7 cm   W: 2.6 cm
C81.468

清供慈菇
「陳」，「鳴遠」印
十八世紀初期
長：6.7厘米　闊：2.6厘米
C81.468

26

Large teapot with rounded shoulder
Seals: Jingxi, Shao Xumao zhi
Late 17th/early 18th century
H: 22.3 cm　W: 20.1 cm
C81.414

圓肩素身壺
「荊溪」,「邵旭茂製」印
十七世紀晚期/十八世紀初期
高:22.3厘米　闊:20.1厘米
C81.414

27

**Teapot of squat round shape with
curved overhead handle**
Seals: Jingxi, Shao Yuanxiang zhi,
Yuanxiang
Late 17th/early 18th century
H: 21.1 cm   W: 20.7 cm
C81.494

鼓腹提梁扁壺
「荊溪」・「邵元祥製」及「元祥」印
十七世紀晚期/十八世紀初期
高：21.1厘米　闊：20.7厘米
C81.494

**Teapot of cylindrical shape with
eight-lobed outer wall pierced with
bamboo motif**
No mark
First half of 18th century
H: 13 cm   W: 9.1 cm
C81.348

玲瓏八竹壺
無款
十八世紀上半葉
高：13厘米　闊：9.1厘米
C81.348

29

Small teapot of squat pear shape, polished
Seals: Hui, Mengchen; Yuanmao
Dated 2nd year of Yongzheng period (1724)
H: 6 cm   W: 7.7 cm
C81.497

磨光束腰孟臣小壺
「惠」，「孟臣」；「元茂」印
「雍正二年甲辰」（1724）作
高：6厘米　闊：7.7厘米
C81.497

30

Small teapot of round shape
Signature: [Hui] Yigong jian zhi
First half of 18th century
H: 5.8 cm   W: 7.3 cm
C81.361

圓腹孟臣小壺
「（惠）逸公監製」刻款
十八世紀上半葉
高：5.8厘米   闊：7.3厘米
C81.361

31 ─────────────

Bowl with appliqué *kui* dragon decoration
Seal: Chen Jinhou zhi
18th century
H: 8.4 cm   D: 20 cm
C81.426

貼花夔龍盌
「陳覲侯製」印
十八世紀
高：8.4厘米　口徑：20厘米
C81.426

32

Teapot of Han square *hu* shape
Seal: Jingyuan Zhai Jichang zhi [Yunli]
18th century
H: 15.9 cm   W: 11.3 cm
C81.363

漢方壺
「靜遠齋繼長製（允禮）」印
十八世紀
高：15.9厘米　闊：11.3厘米
C81.363

33

**Large teapot of Han square *hu* shape
with robin's egg glaze**
Seal: Danran Zhai yin
18th century
H: 22.4 cm   W: 13.8 cm
C81.326

爐均釉漢方壺
「澹然齋印」款
十八世紀
高：22.4厘米　闊：13.8厘米
C81.326

34 ───────────────

**Teapot of round shape with robin's
egg glaze**
Seal: Shanwan
18th century
H: 8.3 cm   W: 15.2 cm
C83.9

爐均釉圓壺
「善玩」印
十八世紀
高：8.3厘米　闊：15.2厘米
C83.9

35 ───────────────

**Teapot with red lacquer coating carved
with archaic dragons on diaper ground**
No mark
18th century
H: 8 cm   W: 17 cm
C85.31

剔紅夔龍紋壺
無款
十八世紀
高：8厘米　口徑：17厘米
C85.31

36

Casket of ancient bronze *fangyi* shape
Seals: Chen Hanwen; Shudai Caotang
baoyong [Zheng Jiang]
First half of 18th century
H: 12.7 cm   W: 14.5 cm
C81.457

仿古「方彝」形蓋盒
「陳漢文」;「書帶草堂保用（鄭江）」印
十八世紀上半葉
高：12.7厘米　闊：14.5厘米
C81.457

37

Large teapot of hexagonal shape with
overhead handle
Seal: Jingxi Xu Bojun zhi
Mid 18th century
H: 30.9 cm   W: 14.7 cm
C81.411

直身提梁六方壺

「荊溪許伯俊製」印

十八世紀中葉

高：30.9厘米　闊：14.7厘米

C81.411

38

Cup of half peach shape lined with silver
No mark
Late 18th/early 19th century
H: 3.3 cm   W: 6.1 cm
C81.432

鑲銀裡桃形盃
無款
十八世紀晚期/十九世紀初期
高：3.3厘米　闊：6.1厘米
C81.432

39

Cup of prunus shape lined with silver
No mark
Late 18th/early 19th century
H: 3.3 cm   W: 6.3 cm
C81.430

鑲銀裡折枝梅花盃
無款
十八世紀晚期/十九世紀初期
高：3.3厘米　闊：6.3厘米
C81.430

40

Teapot decorated with landscape in
famille-rose **enamels**
Seal: Hanzhen
Early 19th century
H: 15 cm W: 12.7 cm
C81.329

粉彩山水竹節壺
「漢珍」印
十九世紀初期
高：15厘米　闊：12.7厘米
C81.329

41

Teapot with slip-painted landscape decoration
Seal: Yang Lüqian
Late 18th century
H: 10.3 cm   W: 10.8 cm
C81.339

泥繪山水圓壺
「楊履乾」印
十八世紀晚期
高：10.3厘米　闊：10.8厘米
C81.339

42

Small teapot with flattened shoulder
Seal: [Feng] Caixia jian zhi
Second quarter of 19th century
H: 5.8 cm   W: 7.2 cm
C81.356

平肩小壺
「（馮）彩霞監製」印
十九世紀上半葉
高：5.8厘米　闊：7.2厘米
C81.356

43

Teapot of stone stele shape encased in pewter
Inscription by Bulang
Dated *ji chou* year of Daoguang period (1829)
H: 11.8 cm   W: 6.8 cm
C81.419

包錫仿碑刻花銘方壺

「步朗製」刻款

「道光己丑」（1829）年刻銘

高：11.8厘米　闊：6.8厘米

C81.419

44

Teapot of trapezoidal grain measure
shape encased in pewter
Seal: Yang Pengnian zhi
Inscription by Boya Ju
Early 19th century
H: 6.9 cm　W: 10 cm
C81.422

包錫刻松銘方斗壺

「楊彭年製」印

「博雅居製」刻款

十九世紀初期

高：6.9厘米　闊：10厘米

C81.422

45

Teapot of oval shape encased in pewter
Seal: Yang Pengnian zao
Inscription by Shimei [Zhu Jian]
Early 19th century
H: 8 cm   W: 8.6 cm
C81.424

包錫刻梅銘圓卵壺
「楊彭年造」印
「石楳（朱堅）」刻銘
十九世紀初期
高：8厘米　闊：8.6厘米
C81.424

46

Teapot of chamfered low cylindrical shape
Seals: [Yang] Pengnian; Amantuo Shi
[Chen Hongshou]
Inscription by Pinjia [Guo Lin]: "Teapot
number 1,379"
Dated *yihai* year of Jiaqing period (1815)
H: 7 cm   W: 11.8 cm
C81.496

直腹刻銘曼生壺
「（楊）彭年」；「阿曼陀室（陳鴻壽）」印
「茗壺第一千三百七十九頻迦（郭麐）」識
「嘉慶乙亥」（1815）年刻銘
高：7厘米   闊：11.8厘米
C81.496

47

Teapot of gourd shape
Seals: [Yang] Pengnian, Jihu
Inscription by Mansheng [Chen Hongshou]
Early 19th century
H: 7.9 cm   W: 10.8 cm
C81.401

半葫蘆形刻銘曼生壺
「（楊）彭年」，「吉壺」印
「曼生（陳鴻壽）」刻
十九世紀初期
高：7.9厘米　闊：10.8厘米
C81.401

48

Teapot of conical shape with engraved bamboo decoration
Seals: [Yang] Pengnian; Hugong Yefu
[Qu Yingshao]
Inscription by Xiaogu [Qu Yingshao]
Early 19th century
H: 7.3 cm   W: 12.9 cm
C81.392

刻竹銘石瓢壺
「(楊)彭年」;「壺公冶父(瞿應紹)」印
「小谷」(瞿應紹)刻款
十九世紀初期
高：7.3厘米　闊：12.9厘米
C81.392

49

**Teapot with engraved bamboo
decoration on cover**
Seals: [Yang] Pengnian, Jihu; Yiyuan
[Qiao Zhongxi]
Inscription by Ziye [Qu Yingshao]
Early 19th century
H: 6.6 cm   W: 11.6 cm
C81.390

刻竹銘扁壺
「（楊）彭年」、「吉壺」；「宜園
（喬重禧）」印
「子冶（瞿應紹）」刻款
十九世紀初期
高：6.6厘米　闊：11.6厘米
C81.390

50

Teapot of gourd shape with prunus
painted in *famille-rose* enamels
Seals: Ji'an [Qu Yingshao]; Ding Jun qing
shang [Zaiquan]
Signature: Xingyouheng Tang Zhuren zhi
[Zaiquan]
Dated *jiyou* year of Daoguang period (1849)
H: 9.1 cm   W: 10.8 cm
C81.400

仿曼生粉彩梅枝刻銘壺
「吉安（瞿應紹）」；「定郡清賞（載銓）」印
「行有恒堂主人（載銓）製」刻款
「道光己酉」（1849）年刻
高：9.1厘米　闊：10.8厘米
C81.400

51

Six tea cups
Seals: Hengshen; Zacheng; Yunhui
Early 19th century
H: 3.1 — 3.7 cm   W: 4.6 — 6.5 cm
C81.515 (1 — 6)

茶盃六件
「亨慎」；「砸成」；「雲會」印
十九世紀初期
高：3.1 — 3.7厘米   闊：4.6 — 6.5厘米
C81.515 (1 — 6)

52

Snuff bottle with slip decoration
No mark
19th century
H: 7.3 cm
C83.4

泥繪山水鼻煙壺
無款
十九世紀
高：7.3厘米
C83.4

53

Snuff bottle with enamel decoration
Seal: [Chen] Mingyuan (spurious)
Dated *ji you* year of Daoguang period (1849)
H: 8.2 cm
C83.6

珐瑯彩繪山水紋圓形鼻煙壺
「（陳）鳴遠」印
「道光己酉」（1849）年製
高：8.2厘米
C83.6

54

Snuff bottle with enamel decoration
No mark
19th century
H: 7.2 cm
C83.5

琺瑯彩繪山水紋鼻煙壺
無款
十九世紀
高：7.2厘米
C83.5

55

Three tea cups encased in pewter
Inscription by Suchuan
19th century
H: 3.3 — 4 cm   W: 5.8 — 6.8 cm
C81.516 (4 — 6)

包錫刻銘套盃三件
「素川」刻款
十九世紀
高：3.3 — 4厘米　闊：5.8 — 6.8厘米
C81.516 (4 — 6)

56

**Teapot of trapezoidal grain measure shape
with engraved bamboo decoration**
Seals: Shen Xi, Cha shu xiang wen
Inscription by Zhuping
First half of 19th century
H: 7.1 cm   W: 10.3 cm
C81.375

刻竹銘方斗壺
「申錫」，「茶熟香溫」印
「竹坪」刻款
十九世紀上半葉
高：7.1厘米   闊：10.3厘米
C81.375

57

Teapot of conical shape with engraved bamboo decoration
Seals: Shen Xi; Hugong Yefu
[Qu Yingshao]
Inscription by Ziye [Qu Yingshao]
First half of 19th century
H: 8 cm   W: 12.7 cm
C81.382

石瓢刻竹銘壺
「申錫」;「壺公冶父（瞿應紹）」印
「子冶（瞿應紹）」刻款
十九世紀上半葉
高：8厘米　闊：12.7厘米
C81.382

58

Teapot of bulging round shape
Seal: [Shao] Daheng
First half of 19th century
H: 10.2 cm   W: 12.7 cm
C81.278

素身鼓腹壺
「（邵）大亨」印
十九世紀上半葉
高：10.2厘米   闊：12.7厘米
C81.278

59

Teapot with decoration of "fish metamorphosing into dragon"
Seal: [Shao] Daheng
First half of 19th century
H: 9.2 cm   W: 12.2 cm
C81.374

魚化龍壺
「（邵）大亨」印
十九世紀上半葉
高：9.2厘米　闊：12.2厘米
C81.374

60

Teapot of globular shape
Seals: [Shao] Youlan mi zhi; [Yuan] Yihe;
Zhen Ji
Inscription by Zhuping
Mid 19th century
H: 12.4 cm   W: 11.1 cm
C81.397

刻銘鼓腹壺
「（邵）友蘭秘製」;「（袁）義和」及
「眞記」印
「竹坪」刻款
十九世紀中葉
高：12.4厘米　闊：11.1厘米
C81.397

61 ——————————

Teapot in imitation of Gongchun's knur-shaped classic
Seal: [Huang] Yulin
Signature: Gongchun
Second half of 19th century
H: 11 cm   W: 13.6 cm
C81.393

仿供春樹瘿壺
「（黃）玉麟」印；「貢春」刻款
十九世紀下半葉
高：11厘米　闊：13.6厘米
C81.393

62

Teapot of squat round shape
Seals: Huang Yulin zuo, Yulin
Second half of 19th century
H: 10.1 cm   W: 13.8 cm
C81.280

素身扁圓壺
「黃玉麟作」，「玉麟」印
十九世紀下半葉
高：10.1厘米　闊：13.8厘米
C81.280

63

**Teapot with belt-like band round
the belly**
Seals: Yangxian Pan Zhimao zhi, Zhimao
Inscription by [Shao] Erquan
Mid 19th century
H: 9 cm   W: 11.3 cm
C81.387

腰帶刻銘圓壺
「陽羨潘志茂製」,「志茂」印
「(邵)二泉」刻款
十九世紀中葉
高：9厘米　闊：11.3厘米
C81.387

64

**Teapot in shape of square seal wrapped
in cloth with enamel decoration**
Seals: Huchi, An
Second half of 19th century
H: 10.5 cm   W: 12 cm
C81.323

加彩印包壺
「壺癡」,「盦」印
十九世紀下半葉
高：10.5厘米　闊：12厘米
C81.323

65

Teapot in shape of square seal wrapped in cloth
Seal: Huchi
Second half of 19th century
H: 11.7 cm   W: 10.8 cm
C81.366

印包方壺
「壺癡」印
十九世紀下半葉
高：11.7厘米　闊：10.8厘米
C81.366

66

Teapot with pewter, brass and copper mounts
Seal: TUNG KING SHUN FACTORY.
WEIHAIWEI. No. 1 in English and Chinese
19th century
H: 9.5 cm   W: 18.4 cm
C86.47

鑲銅錫龍紋圓壺
「威海衛同慶順造」中英文印
十九世紀
高：9.5厘米　闊：18.4厘米
C86.47

67 ——————————————

**Teapot of bulging round shape with
overhead handle**
No mark
Late 19th century
H: 13.9 cm   W: 11.7 cm
C81.335

鼓腹提梁壺
無款
十九世紀晚期
高：13.9厘米　闊：11.7厘米
C81.335

68

**Teapot with overhead handle and
ox-snout cover**
Seals: [Chen] Guangming, Feng
Late 19th century
H: 11.7 cm   W: 11.7 cm
C81.362

提梁刻銘牛蓋蓮子扁壺
「（陳）光明」，「鳳」印
十九世紀晚期
高：11.7厘米　闊：11.7厘米
C81.362

**Pair of pillows each engraved with figure
of lady and calligraphy**
Signature: Dongxi zhi
Inscription and decoration by
Fuhuishuangxiu Ge Zhuren
Late 19th century
H: 11 cm   W: 14.8 cm
C81.458 (A, B)

刻仕女題詩瓦枕一對

「東谿製」刻款

「福慧雙修閣主人」題作

十九世紀晚期

高：11厘米　闊：14.8厘米

C81.458 (A, B)

70 ————————————

**Teapot with bamboo motif and braided
overhead handle**
Seals: Rongqing; a rat and Thai characters
c. 1892
H: 21.1 cm   W: 15.2 cm
C81.347

提梁竹節壺
「榮卿」；泰文鼠紋印
約1892年
高：21.1厘米　闊：15.2厘米
C81.347

71

Teapot of conical shape with engraved floral decoration
Marks: Shengbao; Tiehua Xuan zhi
Inscription by Zhuoyun
Early 20th century
H: 6.8 cm   W: 8.9 cm
C81.309

石瓢刻花銘壺
「生寶」；「鐵畫軒製」印
「琢雲」刻款
二十世紀初期
高：6.8厘米   闊：8.9厘米
C81.309

72 ————————

**Teapot of round shape with
bamboo motif**
Seals: [Fan] Jing'an, Fanzhuang Nongjia
Inscription by Qitao [Wu Hanwen]
dated *gui mao* year (1903)
H: 8.3 cm   W: 12 cm
C81.307

刻果銘竹節壺
「（范）靜安」，「范莊農家」印
「癸卯」（1903）年「跂陶（吳漢文）」刻
高：8.3厘米　闊：12厘米
C81.307

Teapot of conical shape
Seals: [Fan] Jing'an, Fanzhuang Nongjia
Early 20th century
H: 7.2 cm   W: 11.6 cm
C81.296

素身石瓢壺
「（范）靜安」，「范莊農家」印
二十世紀初期
高：7.2厘米　闊：11.6厘米
C81.296

74

Teapot of flower shape
Seal: [Fan] Dasheng
Early 20th century
H: 10.5 cm   W: 13 cm
C81.313

六瓣合菱壺
「（范）大生」印
二十世紀初期
高：10.5厘米　闊：13厘米
C81.313

75

**Teapot of square incense-burner shape
with bulging sides tapering to four legs**
Seals: Baohua An zhi, Tao, Zhai [Duanfang]
Dated 1st year of Xuantong period (1909)
H: 7.6 cm   W: 8.9 cm
C81.522

素身橋頂傳爐壺

「寶華盦製」，「陶」，「齋」（端方）印
「宣統元年（1909）月正元日 」印
高：7.6厘米　闊：8.9厘米
C81.522

76

Teapot of cylindrical shape
Seals: Wang Yinchun, Yinchun
Early 20th century
H: 11.4 cm   W: 9.8 cm
C81.279

素身直壁壺
「王寅春」，「寅春」印
二十世紀初期
高：11.4厘米　闊：9.8厘米
C81.279

77

Teapot of square rectangular shape with bulging sides
Seals: Wang Yinchun, Yinchun
Early 20th century
H: 9 cm   W: 11 cm
C81.276

鼓腹四方壺
「王寅春」,「寅春」印
二十世紀初期
高:9厘米   闊:11厘米
C81.276

78

Teapot of low round shape with
flattened shoulder
Seals: Pei Shimin nian qishiliu zhi,
Shimin, Qishiqi laoren
 c. 1968
H: 8.1 cm   W: 12.7 cm
C81.282

素身裙腳圓壺
「裴石民年七十六製」,「石民」及
「七十七老人」印
約1968年
高:8.1厘米   闊:12.7厘米
C81.282

79

Teapot of dome shape with ox-snout cover
Seals: Pei Shimin, Shimin
Early 20th century
H: 7.5 cm   W: 12 cm
C81.284

牛蓋蓮子壺
「裴石民」,「石民」印
二十世紀初期
高：7.5厘米　闊：12厘米
C81.284

80

Teapot with engraved fruit-and-flower decoration

Seals: [Shao] Guangyu; Nanyang Quanye Hui jinianpin (*ji you* [1909])

Inscription by Songjiu dated *geng xu* year (1910)

H: 11.2 cm   W: 12.2 cm

C81.492

刻松鼠瓜果題詩折肩壺

「（邵）光裕」；「〔己酉（1909）〕
南洋勸業會記念品」印

「庚戌」（1910）年「頌九」刻款

高：11.2厘米   闊：12.2厘米

C81.492

81 ────

Teapot of rectangular shape with bird-and-flower decoration engraved through allover black slip
Seals: Wu Desheng zhi; [Hu] Yaoting
Inscription by Qitao [Wu Hanwen] dated *ren xu* year (1922)
Decoration engraved by Soushi Shi
H: 15.5 cm   W: 7.1 cm
C81.290

黑陶衣刻花鳥銘方壺
「吳德盛製」；「（胡）耀庭」印
「壬戌」（1922）年「跂陶（吳漢文）」刻款
「漱石氏」作梅花小鳥
高：15.5厘米　闊：7.1厘米
C81.290

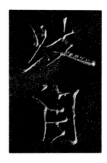

82 ——————————————————————

Teapot with angled shoulder
Seal: Ke Zhai [Wu Dacheng]
Inscription by Dongxi
Early 20th century
H: 10.6 cm   W: 12.8 cm
C81.305

刻銘折肩直身圓壺
「愙齋（吳大澂）」印
「東谿」刻
二十世紀初期
高：10.6厘米　闊：12.8厘米
C81.305

83 ─────────

Teapot of squat round shape
Seals: [Cheng] Shouzhen, Bingxin
Daoren; Zhen Ji; Zhuoru
Signature: Bai Heng jian zhi, dated *ding*
mao year (1867)
Inscription by Zhuoru
H: 10.1 cm   W: 13.9 cm
C81.377

刻銘扁圓壺
「（程）壽珍」,「冰心道人」;
「眞記」;「琢如」印
「丁卯」（1867）年白珩監製
「琢如」刻款
高：10.1厘米　闊：13.9厘米
C81.377

84

Teapot of globular shape
Seals: [Cheng] Shouzhen, Bashier laoren
zou ci minghu Banama Heguo huowupin
Zhanlanhui cengde youjiang; Zhen Ji
c. 1915
H: 13.5 cm   W: 12.6 cm
C81.378

掇球壺
「（程）壽珍」，「八十二老人作此茗壺
巴拿馬和國貨物品展覽會曾得優獎」；
「真記」印
約1915年
高：13.5厘米   闊：12.6厘米
C81.378

85

Teapot of cylindrical shape fitted in
drum-shaped warmer with
bird-and-flower decoration engraved
through black slip
Seals: [Cheng] Pan'gen, Bingxin Daoren
Inscription by Yunshi Shi dated *yi chou*
year (1925)
H: 13.1 cm　W: 14.5 cm
C81.394

刻花銘連溫器套壺
「（程）盤根」‧「冰心道人」印
乙丑（1925）年「雲石氏」刻款
高：13.1厘米　闊：14.5厘米
C81.394

86

Teapot of tall cylindrical shape
Seal: [Feng] Guilin
Dated *jia xu* year (1934)
H: 17 cm　W: 8.6 cm
C81.289

直筒圓壺
「（馮）桂林」印
「甲戌（1934）年置」印
高：17厘米　闊：8.6厘米
C81.289

87

Teapot in shape of Buddha's hand citron
Seal: [Fan] Jinfu
Early 20th century
H: 9.2 cm   W: 18 cm
C81.302

巧色佛手壺
「（范）錦甫」印
二十世紀初期
高：9.2厘米　闊：18厘米
C81.302

88

Palette and water holder in form of square box
Seals: Tiehua Xuan zhi; Kuiting [Jiang Yanting]
Inscription by Fangxue
Early 20th century
H: 5.1 cm   W: 10.8 cm
C81.456

刻梅竹銘調色盒
「鐵畫軒製」;「夔庭（蔣燕亭）」印
「訪雪」刻款
二十世紀初期
高：5.1厘米　闊：10.8厘米
C81.456

89

Teapot of depressed round shape with tall well-railing overhead handle
Seals: Gu Jingzhou, Jingzhou, Zhou;
Lixia Meilin [Han Meilin]
Dated winter of *ding mao* year (1987)
H: 14.8 cm　　W: 14.2 cm
C88.33

刻銘井欄提梁扁壺
「顧景舟」，「景舟」，「舟」及
「歷下（韓）美林」印
「丁卯年（1987）冬景舟美林製於丁山」
刻款
高：14.8厘米　　闊：14.2厘米
C88.33

**Teapot with dragon handle and
three legs**
Seals: Zhou Guizhen, Guizhen (twice)
Inscription by Shiyu [Shen Hansheng]
1980s
H: 11.3 cm   W: 16.5 cm
AC88.46

環龍三足刻銘壺
「周桂珍」,「桂珍」（兩次）印
「石羽（沈漢生）」刻款
1980年代
高：11.3厘米   闊：16.5厘米
AC88.46

91

Bravery subduing lawlessness
Seal: [Xu] Xiutang (twice)
c. 1980
Figure H: 12.5 cm   W: 20 cm
Tray of crab H: 7 cm   W: 12.7 cm
C82.28 (A, B)

勝過橫者在於勇
「（徐）秀棠」（兩次）印
約1980年
像高：12.5厘米　闊：20厘米
蟹座高：7厘米　闊：12.7厘米
C82.28 (A, B)

92

The eccentric monk
Seal: [Xu] Xiutang
Dated *jia zi* year (1984)
H: 48 cm
C86.61

始陶異僧
「（徐）秀棠」印
「甲子」（1984）年作
高：48厘米
C86.61

93 ——————————

Eight miniature teapots
Seals: [Xu] Hantang, Xu Ji
c. 1980
H: 2.2 — 4.3 cm   W: 3 — 4 cm
C82.26 (1 — 8)

集錦小壺八件
「（徐）漢棠」，「徐記」印
約1980年
像高：2.2 — 4.3厘米　闊：3 — 4厘米
C82.26 (1 — 8)

94 ————————————

Figure of Gongchun at work
No mark, most probably made by
Xu Xiutang
c. 1980
H: 26.5 cm   W: 32 cm
C83.13

供春塑像
無款，應爲徐秀棠所製
約1980年
高：26.5厘米   闊：32厘米
C83.13

95

**Water dropper in form of hollow trunk
with perching toad and mole-cricket**
Seals: Jiang, Rong (twice)
c. 1980
H: 7.3 cm   W: 9.4 cm
C81.451

土狗樹蛙水注
「蔣」・「蓉」（兩次）印
約1980年
高：7.3厘米　闊：9.4厘米
C81.451

96

Teapot in form of lotus seed-pod with kingfisher on cover
Seals: [Wang] Yinxian, Yinxian
c. 1980
H: 14 cm   W: 13.2 cm
C82.21

翠鳥蓮蓬壺
「（汪）寅仙」，「寅仙」印
約1980年
高：14厘米　闊：13.2厘米
C82.21

97

Teapot with rounded shoulder and ox-snout cover
Seals: He, Daohong (twice)
1980s
H: 7.4 cm   W: 15 cm
AC88.45

圓肩牛蓋壺
「何」‧「道洪」（兩次）印
1980年代
高：7.4厘米　闊：15厘米
AC88.45

98

Teapot with three legs and arc-like overhead handle
Seals: Li Bifang zhi, Bifang;
Zhang Shouzhi
1980s
H: 17 cm　W: 16.1 cm
C88.39

三足綫紋提梁壺
「李碧芳製」，「碧芳」；「張守智」印
1980年代
高：17厘米　闊：16.1厘米
C88.39

99

Teapot of globular shape with inlaid silver spots
Seals: Bao Zhongmei zhi, Zhongmei, a ram
1980s
H: 9.8 cm   W: 11.8 cm
C88.41

嵌銀片博浪錘壺
「鮑仲梅製」，「仲梅」及羊印
1980年代
高：9.8厘米　闊：11.8厘米
C88.41

100

Teapot of tall square shape with relief
decoration simulating bundled bamboo
Seals: Gu Shaopei zhi, Gu (three times),
Shaopei (twice)
Inscription by Shiyu [Shen Hansheng]
dated *wu chen* year (1988)
H: 17 cm   W: 14.7 cm
C88.40

高風亮節壺
「顧紹培製」‧「顧」（三次）及「紹培」
（兩次）印
「戊辰」（1988）年「石羽（沈漢生）」題
高：17厘米　闊：14.7厘米
C88.40

101

Export teapot of hexagonal shape with appliqué floral scroll
No mark
Late 17th century
H: 10 cm   W: 8.5 cm
C81.482

外銷貼花六方壺
無款
十七世紀晚期
高：10厘米　闊：8.5厘米
C81.482

102 ————————————————————

**Export teapot with appliqué auspicious
decoration of boys and peonies**
No mark
Late 17th century
H: 11.1 cm　W: 9.8 cm
C81.483

外銷貼花富貴多子紋獅鈕壺
無款
十七世紀晚期
高：11.1厘米　闊：9.8厘米
C81.483

103

Export teapot decorated with figures in landscape in relief
Seal: Yunshi Ju
Late 17th/early 18th century
H: 13.5 cm   W: 17 cm
C85.30

外銷淺浮雕山水人物紋壺
「筠石居」印
十七世紀晚期／十八世紀初期
高：13.5厘米　闊：17厘米
C85.30

104

Export teapot of hexagonal shape
No mark
From the Nanking Cargo
c. 1750
H: 13 cm   W: 21 cm
C86.52

外銷獸鈕六方壺
無款
南京貨物之一
約1750年
高：13厘米　闊：21厘米
C86.52

105

Export teapot of pear shape
Signature: Yuxiang Zhai
From the Nanking Cargo
c. 1750
H: 6 cm   W: 11 cm
C86.54

外銷梨形小壺
「玉香齋」刻款
南京貨物之一
約1750年
高：6厘米　闊：11厘米
C86.54

106

Export teapot of phoenix shape
No mark
Mid 18th century
H: 11.2 cm   W: 15.2 cm
C81.369

外銷博山天雞壺
無款
十八世紀中葉
高：11.2厘米   闊：15.2厘米
C81.369

107

Export teapot decorated with
famille-rose **enamels**
Seals: Jingxi, Shao Yuanhua zhi
Late 17th/early 18th century
H: 20.5 cm   W: 18 cm
C83.10

外銷粉彩花卉紋茶壺
「荊溪」,「邵元華製」印
十七世紀晚期/十八世紀初期
高：20.5厘米　闊：18厘米
C83.10

108

Export teapot with appliqué prunus decoration
Seal: Guorui
Early 18th century
H: 10.3 cm   W: 8.2 cm
C81.477

外銷貼梅花方壺
「國瑞」印
十八世紀初期
高：10.3厘米　闊：8.2厘米
C81.477

109 ——————————————

Tankard with appliqué decoration,
English imitation of Yixing ware
No mark, attributed to the Elers brothers
of Staffordshire
Late 17th century
H: 10.6 cm   W: 7.8 cm
C81.486

英國仿宜興貼花直身盃
無款，傳爲斯塔福德郡作坊
埃勒斯兄弟所製
十七世紀晚期
高：10.6厘米　闊：7.8厘米
C81.486

110

**Teapot with appliqué decoration,
English imitation of Yixing ware**
No mark
Mid 18th century
H: 10.8 cm   W: 10.9 cm
C81.479

英國仿宜興貼花人物壺

無款

十八世紀中葉

高：10.8厘米　闊：10.9厘米

C81.479

111

Teapot with appliqué prunus decoration,
Dutch imitation of Yixing ware
Mark: ARY · DE · MILDE · and
galloping horse
c. 1680
H: 11.6 cm   W: 11.2 cm
C81.485

荷蘭仿宜興貼梅花獅鈕壺

ARY · DE · MILDE · 奔馬款
約1680年
高：11.6厘米　闊：11.2厘米
C81.485

112

Teapot with enamel painted decoration, Dutch imitation of Yixing ware
Mark: ARY · DE · MILDE · and galloping horse
Late 17th/early 18th century
H: 14.4 cm   W: 11.2 cm
C81.484

荷蘭仿宜興加彩提梁壺
ARY · DE · MILDE · 奔馬款
十七世紀晚期/十八世紀初期
高：14.4厘米　闊：11.2厘米
C81.484

113

**Coffeepot, Böttger stoneware imitation
of Yixing ware**
No mark
Early 18th century
H: 15.5 cm   W: 7.1 cm
C81.478

德國仿宜興貼花咖啡壺
無款
十八世紀初期
高：15.5厘米   闊：7.1厘米
C81.478

114

**Export teapot of articulated pear shape
with gold mounting and polished for the
Thai market**
Signature: Liupei
Seals: Junde; shuiping
19th century
H: 7 cm   W: 9.7 cm
C86.46

外銷泰國梨形磨光鑲金壺
「留佩」刻款；「君德」及「水平」印
十九世紀
高：7厘米　闊：9.7厘米
C86.46

115

**Export teapot of cylindrical shape
polished for the Thai market**
Mark: Gongju (Tribute Bureau)
Pictorial seal: a dragon
Late 19th century
H: 17.6 cm   W: 11 cm
C81.373

外銷泰國磨光圓筒壺
「貢局」及龍紋印
十九世紀晚期
高：17.6厘米　闊：11厘米
C81.373

116

**Export teapot of squat round shape
polished for the Thai market**
Mark: Lixing
Late 19th century
H: 12.5 cm   W: 18 cm
C83.31

外銷泰國磨光扁圓壺
「利興」款
十九世紀晚期
高：12.5厘米　闊：18厘米
C83.31

117

Export teapot of globular shape with
gold mounting
Seals: Thailand; 125 (both in Thai
characters)
c. 1907
H: 7 cm   W: 12.8 cm
C86.44

外銷泰國鑲金圓壺
「泰國」；「125」泰文印
約 1907 年
高：7 厘米　闊：12.8 厘米
C86.44

118

Export teapot of cylindrical shape with fitted strainer, metal mounts and overhead handle
Seals: Thailand; chongshui (both in Thai characters)
Late 19th / early 20th century
H: 10 cm   W: 8.8 cm
C86.45

外銷泰國附茶隔圓筒提梁壺
「泰國」;「沖水」泰文印
十九世紀晚期/二十世紀初期
高：10厘米   闊：8.8厘米
C86.45

INDEX
索引

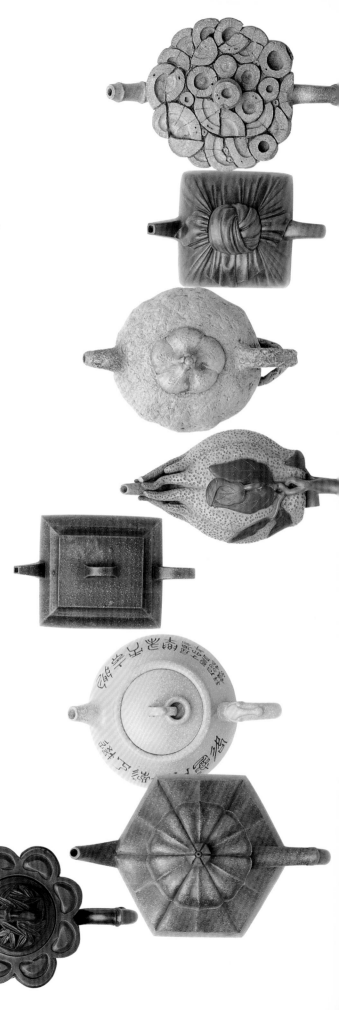

Name Signature/seal	Chinese	Classification	Date	Plate nos
Ary de Milde ARY · DE · MILDE ·		Dutch potter	died 1708	111, 112
Bai Heng Bai Heng jian zhi	**白珩** 白珩監製	potter, inscriber	active second half of 19th century	83
Bao Zhongmei Bao Zhongmei zhi Zhongmei ram	**鮑仲梅** 鮑仲梅製 仲梅 羊印	potter	born 1944	99
Boya Ju Boya Ju zhi	**博雅居** 博雅居製	inscriber	active early 19th century	44
Bulang Bulang zhi	**步朗** 步朗製	inscriber	active 1820s	43
Chen Chen Gongzhi	**陳辰** 共之	potter	active early 17th century	11
Chen Guangming Guangming Feng	**陳光明** 光明 鳳	potter	active late 19th century	68
Chen Hanwen Chen Hanwen	**陳漢文** 陳漢文	potter	active early 18th century	36
Chen Hongshou generally referred to as Chen Mansheng Amantou Shi Mansheng	**陳鴻壽** 一般稱爲陳曼生 阿曼陀室 曼生	scholar-connoisseur, designer, inscriber	1768 – 1822	46, 47
Chen Jinhou Chen Jinhou zhi	**陳覲侯** 陳覲侯製	potter	active c. 1736 – 95	31
Chen Mansheng see Chen Hongshou	**陳曼生** 見陳鴻壽			
Chen Mingyuan Chen Mingyuan Chen Mingyuan Hecun	**陳鳴遠** 陳 鳴遠 陳鳴遠 鶴邨	potter	active mid 17th – early 18th century	18 – 25
Chen Yongqing Yongqing	**陳用卿** 用卿	potter	active c. 1621 – 44	13

Name Signature/seal	Chinese	Classification	Date	Plate nos
Chen Zhongmei Chen Zhongmei zuo	**陳仲美** 陳仲美作	potter	active early – mid 17th century	12
Chen Ziqi Chen Ziqi	**陳子畦** 陳子畦	potter	active c. 1628 – 44	10
Cheng Pan'gen Pan'gen Bingxin Daoren (alternative name of grandfather Cheng Shouzhen)	**程盤根** 盤根 冰心道人 （沿用祖父 程壽珍印章）	potter	active first half of 20th century	85
Cheng Shouzhen Shouzhen Bingxin Daoren Bashier laoren zuo ci minghu Banama Heguo huowupin Zhanlanhui cengde youjiang	**程壽珍** 壽珍 冰心道人 八十二老人作此茗壺 巴拿馬和國貨物品 展覽會曾得優獎	potter	active second half of 19th – early 20th century	83, 84
Cheng Yuncong Yuncong zhi	**承雲從** 雲從製	potter	active c. 1621 – 44	16
Cuizhu Ju	翠竹居	potter (?)	active early 18th century	17
Danran Zhai yin	澹然齋印	potter (?)	18th century	33
Dongxi Dongxi zhi	東谿 東谿製	inscriber	active late 19th – early 20th century	69, 82
Duanfang Baohua An zhi Tao Zhai	**端方** 寶華盦製 陶 齋	scholar- connoisseur	1861 – 1911	75
Fan Dasheng Dasheng	**范大生** 大生	potter	active early 20th century	74
Fan Jinfu Jinfu	**范錦甫** 錦甫	potter	active early 20th century	87
Fan Jing'an Jing'an Fanzhuang Nongjia	**范靜安** 靜安 范莊農家	potter	active late 19th – early 20th century	72, 73
Fangxue	訪雪	inscriber	early 20th century	88

Name Signature/seal	Chinese	Classification	Date	Plate nos
Feng Caixia Caixia jian zhi	馮彩霞 彩霞監製	potter	active c. 1821 – 50	42
Feng Guilin Guilin	馮桂林 桂林	potter	first half of 20th century	86
Fuhuishuangxiu Ge Zhuren	福慧雙修閣主人	inscriber	active late 19th century	69
Gongchun Gongchun	供春 供春	potter	active c. 1506 – 21	1
Gongju	貢局	Tribute Bureau	early 17th – late 19th century	115
Gu Jingzhou Gu Jingzhou Jingzhou Zhou	顧景舟 顧景舟 景舟 舟	potter	born 1915	89
Gu Shaopei Gu Shaopei zhi Gu Shaopei	顧紹培 顧紹培製 顧 紹培	potter	born 1945	100
Guorui	國瑞	potter	active early 18th century	108
Guo Lin Pinjia	郭麐 頻迦	scholar-connoisseur, inscriber	1767 – 1831	46
Han Meilin Lixia Meilin	韓美林 歷下美林	designer	born 1936	89
Hanzhen	漢珍	potter	active late 18th – early 19th century	40
He Daohong He Daohong	何道洪 何 道洪	potter	born 1943	97
Hengshen	亨慎	potter	early 19th century	51
Hu Yaoting Yaoting	胡耀庭 耀庭	potter	active early 20th century	81
Huchi An	壺癡 盦	potter (?)	active second half of 19th century	64, 65

Name Signature/seal	Chinese	Classification	Date	Plate nos
Huang Yulin Huang Yulin zuo Yulin	**黃玉麟** 黃玉麟作 玉麟	potter	active second half of 19th century	61, 62
Hui Mengchen Hui Mengchen	**惠孟臣** 惠 孟臣	potter	active c. 1620 – 44	29
Hui Yigong Yigong jian zhi	**惠逸公** 逸公監製	potter	first half of 18th century	30
Jiang Rong Jiang Rong	**蔣蓉** 蔣 蓉	potter	born 1919	95
Jiang Yanting Kuiting	**蔣燕亭** 夔庭	potter	active early 20th century	88
Li Bifang Li Bifang zhi Bifang	**李碧芳** 李碧芳製 碧芳	potter	born 1939	98
Li Maolin Li Maolin zao	**李茂林** 李茂林造	potter	active c. 1573 – 1620	6
Li Zhongfang Zhongfang	**李仲芳** 仲芳	potter	active c. 1573 – 1620	7
Liupei Junde	留佩 君德	potter (?)	19th century	114
Lixing	**利興**	company	late 18th – late 19th century	116
Nanyang Quanye Hui Nanyang Quanye Hui jinianpin	**南洋勸業會** 南洋勸業會記念品	Nanjing exposition	1909	80
Pan Zhimao Yangxian Pan Zhimao zhi Zhimao	**潘志茂** 陽羨潘志茂製 志茂	potter	active mid 19th century	63
Pei Shimin Pei Shimin Pei Shimin nian qishiliu zhi Shimin Qishiqi laoren	**裴石民** 裴石民 裴石民年七十六製 石民 七十七老人	potter	1892 – 1977	78, 79

Name Signature/seal	Chinese	Classification	Date	Plate nos
Qiao Zhongxi Yiyuan	喬重禧 宜園	scholar-connoisseur	active early 19th century	49
Qu Yingshao Hugong Yefu Xiaogu Ziye Ji'an	瞿應紹 壺公冶父 小谷 子冶 吉安	scholar-connoisseur, inscriber	1780 – 1849	48, 49, 50, 57
Rongqing 　rat and Thai characters	榮卿 泰文鼠紋印	potter	active late 19th century	70
Shanwan	善玩	potter (?)	18th century	34
Shao Daheng Daheng	邵大亨 大亨	potter	first half of 19th century	58, 59
Shao Erquan Erquan	邵二泉 二泉	potter, inscriber	active mid 19th century	63
Shao Guangyu Guangyu	邵光裕 光裕	potter	active early 20th century	80
Shao Wenyin Shao Hengyu zhi	邵文銀 邵亨裕制	potter	active c. 1573 – 1620	15
Shao Xumao Jingxi Shao Xumao zhi	邵旭茂 荆溪 邵旭茂製	potter	active late 17th – early 18th century	26
Shao Youlan Youlan mi zhi	邵友蘭 友蘭秘製	potter	active mid 19th century	60
Shao Yuanhua Jingxi Shao Yuanhua zhi	邵元華 荆溪 邵元華製	potter	active late 17th – early 18th century	107
Shao Yuanxiang Jingxi Shao Yuanxiang zhi Yuanxiang	邵元祥 荆溪 邵元祥制 元祥	potter	active late 17th – early 18th century	27
Shen Hansheng Shiyu	沈漢生 石羽	potter, inscriber	born 1946	90, 100
Shen Xi Cha shu xiang wen Shen Xi	申錫 茶熟香溫 申錫	potter	active c. 1821 – 61	56, 57

Name Signature/seal	Chinese	Classification	Date	Plate nos
Shengbao	生寶	potter	active early 20th century	71
Shi Dabin Shi Dabin zhi Dabin	**時大彬** 時大彬製 大彬	potter	mid 16th – early 17th century	3, 4, 5
Shi Peng Shi Peng	**時鵬** 時鵬	potter	first half of 16th – late 16th century	2
Shuiping	水平			114
Songjiu	頌九	inscriber	active early 20th century	80
Soushi Shi	漱石氏	inscriber	active early 20th century	81
Suchuan	素川	inscriber	19th century	55
Thailand 125	**泰國** 125	country	c. 1907	117, 118
Tiehua Xuan Tiehua Xuan zhi	**鐵畫軒** 鐵畫軒製	company	second half of 19th century – present day	71, 88
Tung King Shun Factory TUNG KING SHUN FACTORY. WEIHAIWEI. No. 1	**威海衞同慶順** 威海衞同慶順造	factory	19th century	66
Wang Yinchun Wang Yinchun Yinchun	**王寅春** 王寅春 寅春	potter	1898 – 1977	76, 77
Wang Yinxian Yinxian	**汪寅仙** 寅仙	potter	born 1943	96
Weiqing Laoren	味清老人	potter (?)	active mid 17th century	14
Wu Dacheng Ke Zhai	**吳大澂** 愙齋	scholar-connoisseur	1835 – 1902	82
Wu Desheng Wu Desheng zhi	**吳德盛** 吳德盛製	company	active early 20th century	81
Wu Hanwen Qitao	**吳漢文** 跂陶	potter, inscriber	active early 20th century	72, 81
Xiang Yuanbian Molin Tang	**項元汴** 墨林堂	scholar-connoisseur	1525 – 90	5
Xu Bojun Jingxi Xu Bojun zhi	**許伯俊** 荊溪許伯俊製	potter	active mid 18th century	37

Name Signature/seal	Chinese	Classification	Date	Plate nos
Xu Hantang Hantang Xu Ji	**徐漢棠** 漢棠 徐記	potter	born 1933	93
Xu Xiutang Xiutang Xiutang	**徐秀棠** 秀棠 秀堂	potter	born 1937	91, 92
Xu Youquan Youquan Youquan fang gu	**徐友泉** 友泉 友泉仿古	potter	active c. 1573 – 1620	8, 9
Yang Lüqian Yang Lüqian	**楊履乾** 楊履乾	potter	active late 18th century	41
Yang Pengnian Pengnian Jihu Yang Pengnian zhi Yang Pengnian zao	**楊彭年** 彭年 吉壺 楊彭年製 楊彭年造	potter	1796 – 1820	44 – 49
Yuan Yihe Yihe	**袁義和** 義和	potter	active second half of 19th century	60
Yuanmao	**元茂**	shop	early 18th century	29
Yunhui	雲會	potter (?)	active early 19th century	51
Yunli Jingyuan Zhai Jichang zhi	**允禮** 靜遠齋繼長製	scholar-connoisseur	1697 – 1738	32
Yunshi Ju	筠石居	potter (?)	active late 17th – early 18th century	103
Yunshi Shi	雲石氏	inscriber	active early 20th century	85
Yuxiang Zhai	玉香齋	potter (?)	active mid 18th century	105
Zacheng	砸成	potter (?)	active early 19th century	51
Zaiquan Ding Jun qing shang Xingyouheng Tang Zhuren zhi	**載銓** 定郡清賞 行有恒堂主人製	scholar-connoisseur	died 1854	50
Zhang Shouzhi	**張守智**	scholar-designer	born 1932	98
Zhen Ji	**真記**	company, potter (?)	mid 19th – first half of 20th century	60, 83, 84

Name Signature/seal	Chinese	Classification	Date	Plate nos
Zheng Jiang Shudai Caotang baoyong	**鄭江** 書帶草堂保用	scholar-connoisseur	1682 – 1745	36
Zhou Guizhen Guizhen	**周桂珍** 桂珍	potter	born 1943	90
Zhu Jian Shimei	**朱堅** 石楳	scholar-connoisseur	active early 19th century	45
Zhuoru	琢如	inscriber	active second half of 19th century	83
Zhuoyun	琢雲	inscriber	early 20th century	71
Zhuping	竹坪	inscriber	active first half of 19th century	56, 60

名稱（按筆劃序）	漢語拼音 / 英文	圖版編號
允禮	Yunli	32
元茂	Yuanmao	29
水平	Shuiping	114
王寅春	Wang Yinchun	76, 77
玉香齋	Yuxiang Zhai	105
生寶	Shengbao	71
申錫	Shen Xi	56, 57
白珩	Bai Heng	83
冲水	Chongshui	118
朱堅	Zhu Jian	45
竹坪	Zhuping	56, 60
亨慎	Hengshen	51
何道洪	He Daohong	97
利興	Lixing	116
吳大澂	Wu Dacheng	82
吳漢文	Wu Hanwen	72, 81
吳德盛	Wu Desheng	81
李仲芳	Li Zhongfang	7
李茂林	Li Maolin	6
李碧芳	Li Bifang	98
步朗	Bulang	43
沈漢生	Shen Hansheng	90, 100
汪寅仙	Wang Yinxian	96
供春	Gongchun	1
周桂珍	Zhou Guizhen	90

名稱（按筆劃序）	漢語拼音／英文	圖版編號
味清老人	Weiqing Laoren	14
承雲從	Cheng Yuncong	16
東谿	Dongxi	69, 82
邵二泉	Shao Erquan	63
邵大亨	Shao Daheng	58, 59
邵元祥	Shao Yuanxiang	27
邵元華	Shao Yuanhua	107
邵友蘭	Shao Youlan	60
邵文銀	Shao Wenyin	15
邵光裕	Shao Guangyu	80
邵旭茂	Shao Xumao	26
南洋勸業會	Nanyang Quanye Hui	80
威海衞同慶順造	TUNG KING SHUN FACTORY. WEIHAIWEI. No. 1	66
胡耀庭	Hu Yaoting	81
范大生	Fan Dasheng	74
范錦甫	Fan Jinfu	87
范靜安	Fan Jing'an	72, 73
徐友泉	Xu Youquan	8, 9
徐秀棠	Xu Xiutang	91, 92
徐漢棠	Xu Hantang	93
時大彬	Shi Dabin	3, 4, 5
時鵬	Shi Peng	2
泰國	Thailand	117, 118
留佩	Liupei	114
眞記	Zhen Ji	60, 83, 84
砸成	Zacheng	51

名稱（按筆劃序）	漢語拼音 / 英文	圖版編號
素　川	Suchuan	55
袁義和	Yuan Yihe	60
貢　局	Gongju	115
國　瑞	Guorui	108
張守智	Zhang Shouzhi	98
訪　雪	Fangxue	88
許伯俊	Xu Bojun	37
郭　麐	Guo Lin	46
陳子畦	Chen Ziqi	10
陳用卿	Chen Yongqing	13
陳仲美	Chen Zhongmei	12
陳光明	Chen Guangming	68
陳　辰	Chen Chen	11
陳漢文	Chen Hanwen	36
陳鳴遠	Chen Mingyuan	18 – 25
陳鴻壽（曼生）	Chen Hongshou(Mansheng)	46, 47
陳覲侯	Chen Jinhou	31
博雅居	Boya Ju	44
善　玩	Shanwan	34
喬重禧	Qiao Zhongxi	49
壺　癡	Huchi	64, 65
惠孟臣	Hui Mengchen	29
惠逸公	Hui Yigong	30
琢　如	Zhuoru	83
琢　雲	Zhuoyun	71
程壽珍	Cheng Shouzhen	83, 84
程盤根	Cheng Pan'gen	85

名稱（按筆劃序）	漢語拼音 / 英文	圖版編號
雲石氏	Yunshi Shi	85
雲　會	Yunhui	51
項元汴	Xiang Yuanbian	5
馮桂林	Feng Guilin	86
馮彩霞	Feng Caixia	42
黃玉麟	Huang Yulin	61, 62
楊彭年	Yang Pengnian	44 – 49
楊履乾	Yang Lüqian	41
筠石居	Yunshi Ju	103
載　銓	Zaiquan	50
頌　九	Songjiu	80
榮　卿	Rongqing	70
漢　珍	Hanzhen	40
漱石氏	Soushi Shi	81
福慧雙修閣主人	Fuhuishuangxiu Ge Zhuren	69
端　方	Duanfang	75
翠竹居	Cuizhu Ju	17
裴石民	Pei Shimin	78, 79
潘志茂	Pan Zhimao	63
蔣　蓉	Jiang Rong	95
蔣燕亭	Jiang Yanting	88
鄭　江	Zheng Jiang	36
澹然齋	Danran Zhai	33
鮑仲梅	Bao Zhongmei	99

名稱（按筆劃序）	漢語拼音 / 英文	圖版編號
韓美林	Han Meilin	89
瞿應紹	Qu Yingshao	48, 49, 50, 57
鐵畫軒	Tiehua Xuan	71, 88
顧紹培	Gu Shaopei	100
顧景舟	Gu Jingzhou	89